PERVERSIONS
of the
SEX INSTINCT

A Study of Sexual Inversion
Based on Clinical Data and Official Documents

by

DOCTOR ALBERT MOLL
Author of Sexual Life of a Child, Hypnotism, etc.

Translated

by

MAURICE POPKIN, Ph.D.

NEWARK
JULIAN PRESS, Inc.
1931

SEXUAL PERVERSION

FOREWORD

The material of which I have availed myself in compiling this book comes from a variety of sources. In the first place my attention was attracted to literature both ancient and modern. My task has been facilitated by the benevolence of the Royal Library of Berlin in placing at my disposal the rich resources which concerned my subject.

My specialization in nervous diseases has furnished me with a part of my observations. The public authorities have also provided me with many cases which were of a particular interest. The State Office has graciously furnished me with judicial records, the study of which has enabled me to discuss the medico-legal side of this question.

But all this would not have sufficed for even a superficial view of my subject. It was also necessary to examine the intimate lives of persons inflicted with sexual perversion. If I have succeeded therein, as I hope, I am indebted to Herr von Meerscheidt-Hullessem, police-inspector, who, with the permission of the president of the Military Police of Berlin, has indicated to me the road to follow. He has served me as guide, accompanying me everywhere, sparing neither time nor energy, and I have been able to amass a great many documents.

I likewise am thankful to all those persons who have aided me in my work. I am indebted especially to the following: Professor Krafft-Ebing of Vienna, for certain literary examples, and for the inspiration which his books have afforded me in conceiving for the most part the idea of this work; Dr. Max Denoir, for his friendly and wise council; and finally, a gentleman whom I shall call N. N. and whom I shall often cite under those initials, himself a sexual invert, living in a large city in the west of Germany and known for his work in other fields. I have many communications from him, not only concerning his sexual life, but also concerning perversion in general. These reports were the more valuable, since N. N. has spent several years in Berlin and since he manifests great impartiality in his observations.

It is useless to say that the observations brought together in the manner just indicated, or delivered to me by the authorities, have been the materials only of this book. The conclusions that I have drawn from them are strictly mine and consequently I am solely responsible for them.

DR. ALBERT MOLL.

CONTENTS

Chapter I

SEXUAL INVERSION

Love, Sensual and Platonic; Pederasty and Uranism; Psycho-Sexual
Hermaphrodism.

Humanity is composed of two sexes: masculine and feminine, differing from each other physically as well as psychically. The physical differences exist principally in the form of the genitals; and from the psychic point of view, there are numerous details which emphasize this differentiation. The occupations of men differ considerably from those of women. In certain lines of endeavor, men find their place more easily than women; on the other hand, women are superior to men in various aptitudes, such as are applied in the execution of many forms of manual labor. Women like adornment, and in this respect are much vainer than men. Among all these psychic properties, which differentiate the two sexes, the sexual instinct does not occupy the last place. In the man it manifests itself during a long period of life in the form of a strong attraction which leads him to seek physical contact with the other sex—a contact of which the climax is the act of coition. The awakening of this instinct takes place at different times under normal conditions; biologically it ought not appear before the advent of puberty.

11

The sexual instinct is found not only in Man but also in the animal. However, the sexual life of Man is distinguished from that of animals by the existence between man and woman of a deeper and more intimate relationship which finds its highest expression in love. It is true that in animals there are to be found between male and female ties of affection which are stronger than those usually to be found in casual matings, but these bonds do not reach the fullness of expression characteristic of man.

However, Man does not appear to have known true love in all epochs nor among all peoples. It is only with the progress of civilization and with the beginnings of sedentary life that Man felt a sexual urge, and then love. Fichte considers the segregation of the sexes as a means of conserving the species. We also shall consider the sexual instinct as a means for assuring the reproduction of the individual. It was Jean-Paul who said that Heaven confided the creation of the world to the motivating power of love.

Under normal conditions love and the sexual instinct do not manifest themselves until after puberty but sometimes certain sentiments make their appearance even during childhood. According to Ramdohr, certain indications of love for women may be found in little boys; among these indications jealousy and the desire for exclusive possession of a woman play a preponderant role. Many men relate that they were as boys attracted to women. This phenomenon has even been regarded as a no uncertain sign of genius. As examples of precocious love may be cited; Dante who loved at the age of nine years, Canova who was smitten at five, and the poet Byron who at eight years fell in love with Mary Duff. Love is often confounded with the sexual instinct. The latter necessitates only the satisfaction of an urge to experience the voluptuous sensations accompanying coition. In this case, there is no question of love; love exists only when, during sexual intercourse, the lover's heart feels itself attracted toward that of the beloved, and when the two lovers feel a sympathetic bond uniting them. It manifests itself in a strong bond which unites the two persons, and which ought to be absolutely distinguished from friendship. This affinity of souls soon leads to a desire for the satisfaction of the senses, or the sexual act, with the beloved. This psychic urge may precede the sexual instinct for a long time; and on the other hand love may develop after sexual relations. It is as yet a moot question whether love can last a long time without the manifestation of the sexual instinct as it is contended in the case of platonic love of which we shall speak later. Perhaps this question will never be answered to the complete satisfaction of all parties.

In all cases love presents a two-fold aspect: a sensual and a psychic. Even though there exists a period in the development of young men and women during which love appears to be purely spiritual it does not persist so for long, and the sexual urge temporarily held in abeyance is not slow in coming to the surface. Hensinger in his treatise on physical and psychic anthropology thus expresses himself: "It is certain that the chaste woman who ardently falls into the strong arms of the man who desires her is thereby unpolluted in her sexual desires, whatever be the attraction exercised over her by this man—to the conclusion of all others; the man, generally more sensual, has a clearer consciousness of his desire, but then he has no longer the right to speak of the purity of his love." Vorlander is entirely of this opinion, though personally I believe that this complete unconsciousness of all sensual desire does not last long.

What differentiates love as an abstraction from the purely sensual urge is the fact that it is addressed sooner to an individual of the other sex than to the other sex in general. As a result, the intimate union found in love is formed between two persons on condition that the love of one is shared by the other. In this case the two feel themselves strongly attached to each other. To be happy love ought to be shared. Carus is right in declaring that among civilized people the desire to be loved amounts to a passion, and that this desire dominates those **who really love.**

Sexual love ought to be clearly separated from all other bonds which can attach individuals to each other. and it constitutes a phenomenon quite different from friendship. In friendship, the sexual functions play no role whatever, while they enter decidedly in love. It is difficult to find the bases of love and the sexual instinct. One may be sure of the fact that the predisposition for the two is congenital. It is difficult to appreciate the role played by external impressions and casual circumstances in the development of each.

Normally, love and the sexual instinct attract man to woman, but there is a class of men with other desires, who feel themselves attracted to man. This attraction for individuals of the same sex is called *homosexuality,* in contradistinction to *heterosexuality* which designates the normal attraction of one sex for the other. To indicate the phenomenon of homosexuality, Westphal uses the term "sexual perversions," which considerably enlarges the field in question. His use of such a term implies a conception of homosexuality which substitutes the sensations of an individual making him feel estranged from his own sex—for the deviation from the sexual instinct itself. In his opinion sexual perversions also include those cases in which the sexual instinct remaining normal through individual presents certain tendencies belonging to the other sex.

The urge which attracts man to man ought to be called *perversion* in the sense that Krafft-Ebing gives to that word. He believes that a perversion is any manifestation of the sexual instinct which is not in accordance with the biological purpose of reproduction. He also draws attention to the necessity of establishing a rigorous distinction between *perversion* and *perversity.* The term *perversion* applies to the sexual instinct when it is perverted, while a perversity arises from a depraved action, without taking into account the power that motivated that action. It is greatly to the credit of Krafft-Ebing for having so clearly defined the two conceptions. A perversion is a desire that is independent of volition and for which no one can be held responsible in the eyes of an impartial judge. On the contrary, perversity, which manifests itself in action, ought often to be laid at the door of the individual in point of blame. It can be seen to what point confusion between these two terms has made difficult a true evaluation of sexual inversion, by an examination of the idea propounded by Chevalier to the effect that in acquired sexual perversion, the perversion is dependent on the will of the individual. There is nothing more false than this assertion, as we have just demonstrated. The term pederast is often used to designate those men who exhibit homosexual tendencies. However, I shall not, in general use this term, for scientifically it designated only a certain group of these individuals; that is, those who place *membrum in anum;* it likewise indicates a well defined species of genital act among men, namely, *immissio penis in anum.* The word has deviated from its original meaning. The word pederast comes from *paidos erastes* signifying lover of boys. It was used in a general sense by the ancient Greeks to signify lovers of boys and of young men, whether or not their relations included a sexual act. The relations between two individuals of the masculine sex was also called *commasculatio.* The term of *Uranists* is often encountered in modern literature to designate men with homosexual tendencies. I shall also apply that to such men in the course of this book; and like Krafft-Ebing and other authors, I adopt it because of its brevity.

The term of uranist was introduced by Ulrichs. The word may be derived from Uranus. A passage in Plato's Banquet (chapters VIII and IX) seems to strengthen the idea. "Aphrodite and Eros are one. Two goddesses exist; the older Aphrodite, not born of mother: she is the daughter of Uranus, and we therefore call her Urania; the younger Aphrodite, daughter of Zeus and Diona: we call her Pandemos. The first Eros should consequently be called Uranus, the second, Pandemos. . . . Ordinary men love with the love of Eros Pandemos; on the contrary, Eros of Urania prefers the masculine part to the feminine; and such is the love for boys. That is why individuals animated by this love are attracted to the masculine sex."

A uranist does not experience any voluptuous sensation whatever in the presence of the most beautiful woman, even though he may recognize her beauty. Beauty evidently awakens the sexual desires, but it is quite different from beauty considered purely from an esthetic viewpoint. Even though a uranist gaze casually on a beautiful woman, and does so with pleasure, we cannot in such a case speak of sexual sensations, because he does not at all experience any sexual reflex. It is important at this point to insist on the following characteristic: the uranist possesses all the attributes of virility; his genital organs, penis as well as testicles, are absolutely normal so far as their external form and functions are concerned.

Many reasons point to the fact the desire experienced by Uranists for men has nothing in common with friendship. There is here involved a sexual urge which under normal conditions attracts man to woman. The genitals play a prominent role in the attraction which Uranists feel for men. The Uranist is excited not only by the sight of the genitals of man, but even by the thought of them. It is the desire of a Uranist to commit some kind of sexual act through contact with another man.

The foregoing facts are sufficient to indicate that the Uranistic tendency is only a form of the sexual instinct; but this characteristic has a much clearer basis in other manifestations, such as jealousy which accompanies the love of a Uranist. Jealousy is never encountered in true friendship; never is the bond which unites two friends such that the acquisition of a new friend by one is regarded angrily by the other. Quite otherwise is love among men; here jealousy reigns supreme. Similar to the love of man for woman is the love of the Uranist for the beloved person. He will not share him with anybody else; his anger is unlimited for anyone who seeks to possess the object of his love.

The sexual attraction exercised by a man on another may manifest itself in various ways. In certain cases a man is excited only by another man. Such is an affair between Uranists in the narrow sense of the word. At other times the man is attracted now by a man, now by a woman, and then again by both at the same time .

He who experiences a desire for women as well as for men is called a psychosexual *hermaphrodite*.

According to Ramsdohr, homosexual tendencies are found among the animals. Krauss thinks that indications of pederasty are found not only in man, but also in the dog, and in the monkey. N. N., of whom we have spoken in the preface, has told me of a case of two male dogs who rubbed against each other until one of them ejaculated.

It is certain that in sexual perversions there is no question of a casual fact but of a clearly pathological phenomenon, occurring (without premeditation) in certain well-defined conditions. It occurred at all times and in all countries among peoples living in absolute ignorance of each other. That which likewise proves that this phenomenon is controlled by natural laws is the surprising resemblance, the strict analogy found in a great number of biographies and autobiographies of Uranists. Despite quite plausible individual differences there exist in them many common traits which we may consider as characteristic of Uranism.

In the present state of science one can no longer deny the existence of sexual sensations of a feminine nature among men whose genital organs are normally formed. Only, one should not, by using this as a basis, convert an exception into a rule and declare with Hoessli that the external signs of the sex life are superfluous and even negligible in the psychic determination of sex.

Chapter II

AN HISTORICAL SURVEY

Bible and Inversion; Pederasty in Ancient Greece; Friendship and Inversion; Supression of Pederasty; Greek Love in Rome; Inverted Rulers of Rome; Nero, Adrian and Heliogabalus; Literature and Pederasty; Inverted Love in the Church; Inversion in Asia; Study of Inversion; Ulrich and Inversion; Male Prostitution; Historic Inverts; James I and Rudolph II, etc.; Michangelo, Man of the Behind; Inversion and Murder.

The phenomena of sexual perversion or love of man for man, are found in the most ancient of times. Even the Bible includes several passages alluding to this subject. There is no doubt that among the Hebrews, the relations of man to man, stigmatized as criminal or immoral, disappeared because of such stigma.

Indeed, it seems that during all periods and among all peoples, the love of man for man was as widespread as the social position of woman was low. Among the ancient Jews the woman enjoyed, without a doubt, a certain degree of respect, and their family life was even then exemplified because of its purity. The universal reprobation which the love of man for man met among the ancient Jews is not surprising and ought to surprise us the less by reason of the fact that for this people a numerous progeny was considered as the chief aim in life. Many passages in the Bible confirm this. In the book of Judges, the daughter of Jeptha considered it a shame to die without leaving children.

Moses likewise attributed great importance to a rich pos-
terity: the people of Israel had to multiply as the sands of
the sea. A numerous progeny was, for Moses, the greatest
good fortune a man could desire, and in his opinion sterility
constituted a calamity. Onan was renounced for having
spilled his semen on the ground. Abortion, according to
Flavius Joseph, was punishable by death. Among other peoples who did not consider a numerous progeny as the principal aim in life, it was judged much less severely. For a
similar reason abortion was permitted, according to Ploss,
among the ancient Greeks in certain circumstances, when for
example the child had not yet reached that point in its foetal
development when the mother is said to "feel life." It was
also widespread in Rome.

We find parrallel with these ideas on abortion and numerous descendants, another among the ancient Jews. It was
their great horror for homosexual love. The Bible apprises
us of the fact that when the inhabitants of Sodom wished to
consort sexually with the angels who descended to the pious
Lot, God in His wrath entirely destroyed their city. Such is
the origin of the expression Sodomy which we use rather frequently nowadays to designate certain types of sexual intercourse between men (immissio membrum in anum) or between men and animals. In the third book of Moses, the
Lord says to him, "If a man lie with mankind as he lieth with
a woman, both of them have committed an abomination:
they shall surely be put to death; their blood shall be upon
them."

In ancient times, Asia was considered the birthplace of
pederasty, and even today it is generally admitted that in the
Orient, pederasty manifests itself more clearly and is to be
found perhaps more often than in the Occident; only we
ought to observe that the weaker manifestations of Uranism
does not imply its less frequent existence for intercourse between men remains secret very often, without the slightest
external sign of its existence. I ought therefore to call attention to this error since I know men in public office who prac-

tice coition only with men without the slightest suspicion on the part of outsiders. Be that as it may, the Orient has always been considered the birth-place of pederasty and if one is to agree with Tarnowsky, it was from Armenia that it spread later to the Orient. This is explained by the fact (again according to Tarnowsky) that the inhabitants of Armenia, like many other mountaineers, are not free from certain well-defined marks of psychic degeneracy and thus offer a field particularly favorable for the flourishing of sexual perversions.

In examining another civilized people of antiquity, namely the Greeks, we shall discover the love of man for man practiced to a great extent among them. Although in ancient mythology there is hardly any mention of love between males, several more recent authors have sought to find in this love the basis for certain myths.

The intercourse between Jupiter and Ganymede was considered by the ancient Greeks as an example of love for boys; numerous passages allude to it. Nevertheless, Xenophon says in his Banquet that Jupiter had raised Ganymede to Olympus because of his "soul." But, according to the context, there is no doubt that the bonds which existed between the god and the young man were those of love and not simply those of friendship. In his "Phædrus," Plato is much more explicit on the subject of Jupiter and Ganymede. He comes to the point when he speaks of their amorous dalliance, at the end of a chapter dealing with the physical contact between lovers in the gymnasiums. Another argument in favor of this interpretation of the intercourse between Jupiter and Ganymede is found in the fact that the legend as reported by Plato in his "Laws" was promulgated in the isle of Crete where pederasty was very widespread. The relations between Apollo and Hyacinthus, and between Hercules and Hylas were similarly interpreted. The close friendship between Achilles and Patroclus was very often considered as true love. It is true that Homer speaks of the strong friendship that united the two Greeks, but, in my opinion, there is noth-

ing in the passages alluding to them that Homer thought of
them as lovers. Aeschinus seeks to interpret Homer's terms
in an erotic sense, and later we often find this interpretation.
In the "Myrmidons" of Aeschylus, Achilles deplores the death
of Patroclus in terms that smack of more than pure friendship.
However, Welker does not admit the erotic interpretation of
Achilles' lamentations. In his "Banquet," Plato speaks of
Alceste's love for her husband, and immediately thereafter
establishes an analogy between this love and that which existed between Patroclus, called *erastes* of Achilles, and Achilles
very often called *eromenos* of Patroclus. Xenophon, in his "Banquet," interprets the intercourse between the two quite otherwise
—as friendship. Here Patroclus is called the *hetairos* of Achilles.
The Greeks mentioned many other mythological figures to
prove the existence of pederasty in the most ancient of times,
and in doing so, they tended towards exaggeration. Thus
the relations between Orestes and Pylades, and between
Thesus and Peyrithous were considered those of love as well
as those of friendship. According to Mantegazza, an ancient
author would have it that Achilles killed Troilus, son of
Priam, only after the latter refused to accede to his passion.

If one wishes to study the love between men and boys as
it existed in Greece during historic times, it would be appropriate to pass in review the different parts of the country
and to examine each part separately. I shall begin with
Athens where by unanimous opinion the love for young men
was most widespread, although as we have just said, pederasty was perhaps more widespread in the isle of Crete than
in Athens itself.

Even then, the laws of Solon recognized pederasty after
a fashion. In speaking of the laws of Solon, we speak only
of those attributed to him, for in the opinion of historians
of the first rank there are some of which he was not the
author. In these laws pederasty was subjected to certain restrictions which applied principally to slaves, and which allowed a certain latitude of action to the free Athenians.

The *logoi erotichoi* which constituted an important part of ancient Greek literature, devoted itself to pederasty to a great extent. We know that in Athens there were even temples in honor of Eros, the protector of love between men. Atheneus tells us that Charmos, the lover of Hippias, had an altar erected to Eros, at the entrance to the gymnasium of the Academy. Venus Urania also had many temples at Athens. The barber shops and baths were the principal sources of pederasty in Athens, in the sense that men made each other's acquaintance there. But it was also in the gymnasiums, especially on the apparatus, that the admiration of masculine beauty took on more and more the character of love, being accompanied by coquetry, posing, bursts of enthusiasm, jealousy and complete forgetting of ideas of morality (Arnold Hug). Many authors, Aristophanes in his "Clouds," Plato in his "Laws," Plutarch in his "On Love," insisted on connection between love for boys and the physical exercise in the gymnasiums. Plato in his "Phaedrus" says very explicity that there was physical contact between lovers in the gymnasiums and elsewhere. We are in a position to cite other examples of this love in Athens. One is that of Callias who, rising even to the dignity of chief magistrate, loved Autolykos; and their love is made the subject of a comedy by Eupolis, called "Autolykos." The same Callias is burlesqued also by Aristophanes in his "Birds" and in his "Frogs." But according to Ramsdohr, Aristophanes exploited these depraved habits only to provoke laughter and therefore should not be regarded as a judge by virtue of his treatment of them in his comedies. In a way, there is no obscurity in the fact that Aristophanes abused the established customs. His purpose in doing so is only incidental, so far as we are concerned. Among the ancient writers who have written on this theme, let us mention Lysias the celebrated orator, Plutarch who mentions it more than once, saying for example, that in Themistocles' time, pederasty was widespread among the Athenians. Aristotle is the author of passages dealing with love for boys. Again, there is Chevalier who observes that even Hippocrates' sermon proves the existence of pederasty during this period, since in

it are to be found passages in which the physician abjures
sexual intercourse with women, sons of freemen, and slaves.

The most important documents in our possession which
deal with pederasty in the epoch in question are without
doubt furnished by Plato's "Banquet" and "Phaedrus" and by
Xenophon's "Banquet." In them are discussed the relations
between many philosophers and their pupils. Ramsdohr,
among others, thinks that Plato's and Xenophon's intentions
in their "Banquets" were to liberate Socrates of the reproach
of having sexual contact with boys and with young men. And
in fact, in this spirit were conceived the conversation, and
above all, the argument of Socrates in which he always insists
on the spiritual element in love.

I do not understand how pederasty as touched on in Plato's
and Xenophon's "Banquets" could be mistaken for friendship between master and pupils. No doubt there is in these
writings a divergence between the views of certain persons
on pederasty; but the point in question is to know whether
the relations between two men, arising from love, ought to
have spiritual or physical love as their basis. This distinction
is not without interest, for today this form is as formerly to
be met with in the love of man for man. In fact, there exists
a form of Uranism in which the sexual urge is entirely absent
and in its place there is substituted a purely spiritual sentiment of being the sole possessor of the beloved, in which
jealousy plays an important role.

I believe that the "Banquet" and the other writings of the
ancients naturally remains obscure for those who have not
made a study of sexual perversions. How is one to understand, without such study, in the existence in the same individual of love for women and love for men?

The way Alcibiades expresses himself in Plato's "Banquet"
on the subject of his intercourse with Socrates shows us
quite clearly with what little moderation men loved in the
Greek style. Without doubt, the work in question shows us how
the *andreia* and the *sophrosyne* of Socrates prevented him from
having sexual intercourse with Alcibiades, although the latter

exhibited his physical beauty before him. Alcibiades boasts of the subtleties he practiced in seducing Socrates by whom he believed himself loved; it is quite characteristic of the customs which then existed in Athens. Even if we admit that Socrates had no sexual relations with men, it may none the less be deduced from other passages in Plato's "Banquet" that pederasty had quite a sensual characteristic.

If the writings just mentioned devoted themselves to the relations between Socrates and Alcibiades, we know through other classic works that Alcibiades had a great number of lovers during his youth, and that, in the words of Cornelius Nepos, he was loved in the Greek fashion. There is a conflict of opinion in regard to Socrates' habits. In Plato's "Banquet" Socrates declares himself to be a judge only of the subject of love, but the development of this theme shows that it is not precisely the sexual acts that are here designated by the name of love. Socrates explains Eros by his desire to influence the young. Haller judges Socrates a little severely. According to him, Socrates was a debauched philosopher who always preached virtue but who in reality practiced pederasty. It is also told that a well known courtesan compelled Socrates to love Alcibiades. Finally, in his dialogue called "Alcibiades" Aeschinus, disciple of Socrates, speaks at length upon the influence of Socrates on Alcibiades. In any case, Socrates' reputation was quite questionable as regards his intercourse with men. Here, moreover, is what Becker says in his "Introduction to Xenophon's 'Banquet'":

"In examining all the circumstances contributing to Socrates' condemnation, it seems that his being accused of perverting the habits of his young friends had great weight. Examples of his misconduct were even brought forward. Critias and Alcibiades, two well known debauchees, were among his pupils. Among all the accusations brought against Socrates, that of perverting and corrupting young people held first rank. Thus Amytos and Melitos reproached him for the enthusiasm he evinced at the sight of good-looking boys as though it were a crime.   It is quite likely that this accusation contributed much to Socrates' death."

Pausanias explains himself quite clearly on the subject of pederasty in Plato's "Banquet."   He tries to characterize this kind of love as on a high plane, and even declares that those who do not love in the manner of Eros of Urania, that is to say, who do not love men but women, seek only to satisfy a vulgar desire.   It appears also from Pausanias' discourse that during this period boys were inadequately protected against the pederastic practices of mature men.   Pausanias would have looked with favor upon laws forbidding sexual intercourse with boys but it would have been quite characteristic of Pausanias to wish these laws revoked, by reason of the fact that the lover of a boy does not know as yet whom he loves and that, therefore, in so doing he would lose time and energy in pursuing a useless love.

It should not be thought that pederasty manifested itself equally during all periods in Athens.   There were times when it was severely censured.   In this respect the opinions forwarded by the ancient authors are a bit contradictory.   But when certain philologists deny, in a formal way, the physical aspect of love for boys, it is because they are entirely ignorant of the love that exists between men; and as a result, it appears to them inadmissable.   They also seek to interpret the passages devoted to this question in another way, and sometimes they do so in such a forced manner that an impartial observer would be amused with their entirely artificial explanations.   I am not sufficiently versed in the ancient lanluages to give an exact interpretation of all the passages I have found.   But it remains none the less a fact that purely physical love for boys was well known and practiced in ancient times.   It is absolutely impossible to interpret otherwise, the conversations in Plato's "Banquet" and "Phaedrus" and Xenophon's "Banquet."   It may be asked whether Plato and Socrates themselves practiced pederasty, for the discussion is always possible where individuals are concerned.   The writings of ancient authors leave no doubt as to the existence of sexual intercourse between men. Since Greek authors do not describe the sexual act in detail, it does not follow that it did not exist. The same thing applies to the lives between man and woman: the description of the act is usually taboo, but **we none the less conclude** that it exists in persons in whom we witness the concomitant spiritual sentiments of love. If at times, certain descriptions, such as those of modern naturalists, go a little too far, it is not less true that the subject is generally treated with the greatest descretion.

Pederasty was widespread not only in Athens but also in other Greek states. Pausanias' discourse in Plato's "Banquet" tells us that in Elides and in Beotin, relations between men were not forbidden. Cicero confirms these facts by saying that in Elides and in Thebas anything connected with love for boys was permitted. Cicero's recital appears much more accurate when, in regard to it, one examines what took place among the Lacedaemonians, who were permitted to love boys but who were forbidden to have sexual intercourse with them. This passage of Cicero's is a bit obscure, for he adds that in so far as it concerned men embracing and lying together it was allowed in Lacedaemonia. It may be asked whether such conduct was compatible with the absence of the sexual act, properly so called: physical contact pushed to such an extreme, can hardly be thought of without an afterthought of coitus. (It is N. N.'s supposition that the prohibition was exercised only in the case of the *immissio in anum,* everything else being permitted.) It is the contention of certain ancient authors that love between men was least widespread among the Lacedaemonians. Thus, according to Xenophon's "Banquet," those among them who desired the physical possession of men they loved were reputed incapable of noble and good actions. On the other hand, we are in a position to admit with certain ancient authors that physical pederasty was rather widespread among the inhabitants of Elides and of Thebes. Xenophon tells us that among these peoples the lovers slept together; such an action was considered shameful in the other Greek cities. Certain authors even entertain the idea that the famous, sacred legion of three hundred Thebans consisted of warriors with their lovers. Xenophon goes to the extent of saying that in Beotia pederasty was looked upon in the light of a matrimonial union.

Among another group of Greeks, the Ionians (a name ordinarily used to designate the inhabitants of Asia Minor), pederasty was considered a vice of a very infamous sort. We also see Pausanias, in Plato's "Banquet," expressing the opinion that in barbarous countries like that of Ionians pederasty was suppressed. He claims that barbarians disapprove of pederasty just as they do scientific studies and physical development. Despots are not pleased with the idea of forming, among their subjects, a substantial sort of friendship, which might become a source of love for boys. Such friendships have often spelled misfortune for tyrants. It was thus that the love which united Aristogiton and Harmodius caused an eclipse in their power. Various authors and particularly Plato in his "Banquet" have apprised us of the fact that Harmodius was the lover of Aristogiton. This aspect of love between men, so dangerous to tyrants, is also confirmed by another author, namely, Athenius; he cites a whole dynasty of despots who have learned at their own expense of the dangers that may befall them and which are derived from such love. Thus it was that the love of Chariton for Melanippas heaped dangers upon the head of Phalaris of Agrigentes; and thus it was likewise that Polyerates of Tamos destroyed the gymnastic apparatus, one of the principal places in Athens, where pederasty flourished.

We have just reviewed pederasty in several of the Greek states. I must allude to the island of Crete as the place most celebrated for the extent to which love between men was practiced; Aristotle, Atheneas and a great number of other authors often speak of it. In Crete, boys were literally ravished, and what is more, boys of good families were considered as dishonored if they had no lovers. Perhaps there also pederasty did not begin as sexual intercourse. It was only after war with the Persians that the debauch became extraor-

dinary, so much so in regard to sexual intercourse with boys
that the reputation of the isle of Crete became proverbial.

In concluding this chapter, I wish to cite several poets who
have sung of love between men. The "Odes" of Anacreon include a great many passages which throw much light on the
question with which we are occupied. In his ode "To the
Swallow" he complains of the fact that the bird with its sing-
ing disturbs his dreams of Batylles in the morning. In another ode he describes his friend Batylles: his hair is black
and shining, his neck of ivory, and his hips as fair as those
of Pollux:

> Between his fine thighs,
> His thighs full of joy
> I effect with modesty an immodesty
> Which e'en now love aspires.

Further on in the same ode, there is another passage which
already refers directly to pederasty:

> Thine art is quite jealous
> For his back, so well formed
> Doth hide therein all that is best.

Theocritus also sings the praises of love between men in
his "Idylls." In the twelfth, he asks: "Com'st thou, Aitos,
well beloved? Shall the third morning after three nights
take thee from me? Oh, young man, desire makes old men
of us in a single day!—Oh, may the same gods of love be
favorably inclined to us two!"

Whatever be the opinion one entertains of the poets who
have sung of love, surely that if they themselves were not
pederasts, they at least came face to face with those whose
passions they proclaim. Consequently, it is a matter of entire indifference to us whether or not the poet himself was a
lover of men. Let us here recall the following aphorism of
Lessing. In speaking of love as rhapsodized by the poets, he
says that it is the poets' duty to follow the fashion of his gen-
eration. It is his belief that Horace could entertain no other

opinion than that held by his contemporaries. "The poet," says Lessing, "ought to experience sensations, in order to awaken them."—Ought he therefore to have emptied all the glasses and embraced all the girls to sing of them in his poetry?"

It is justly judged of the Greeks that among them pederasty and respect for women were, so to speak, in inverse ratio. Among them women enjoyed, without dispute, little esteem, while pederasty was extensively practiced. Modern moralists, who, whenever the occasion presents itself, preach as rigorous a segregation of the sexes as possible will be surprised to hear that in no place was this separation enforced as in Greece and that nowhere else was modesty so greatly protected. Among the ancient Greeks, true love for woman rarely existed; it was not frequently that a man sacrificed his life to save a woman's while, on the contrary, this trait of true love and of abnegation was not rare among men who loved each other.

Despite the flourishing of pederasty in Greece, it was never considered as the only enviable satisfaction of the sexual instinct. The propogation of the species was not a matter of indifference to the Greeks, and celibacy, despite pederasty, was forbidden. Thus, in Sparta, the laws of Lycurgus inflicted humiliating punishment on celibates. In Athens and in Corinth, similar laws also prevailed and celibates were refused the usual funeral rites.

During the period that pederasty flourished in Greece, little of it was practiced in Rome, at least according to the ancient authors. It is rarely found during the early years of the Roman Republic. According to Randohr it was not the same after the Punic wars. In Carthage, pederasty appears to have been very widespread. It is interesting to note that it did not begin to manifest itself on a large scale among the Romans, until the wars had taught them the customs of the Carthaginians. But, during the last years of the Republic when the vice of the concubines became quite extensive pederasty began to decline. Although certain passages taken

from authors and poets show us that it was already known
in Rome during the Republic pederasty never enjoyed the
same degree of tolerance and even of consideration as it did
in Athens. Besides, it was often known in Rome as "Greek
love."

Even before Rome fell under the domination of the Caesars
we find facts indicating that love between men already existed there. Thus Veturus, slave of Platius, was punished
by his master for having refused him his favors (Dionysius,
Valerius Maximus). According to Polybius it was possible
towards the middle of the second century B. C. to buy a boy
in Rome for a *talent*. However, intercourse with boys was
forbidden by law, notably by that of Scatinius, but authors
are not in accord on the severeness of the penalty decreed by
this law. Cicero mentions this subject frequently. In his
"Tusculanes" he says that disrobing in public led to shameful acts; Greek gymnasiums developed this habit. The ab-
duction of Ganymede as sung by the poets was also related,
according to him, to pederasty; only, one must distinguish
between love and friendship, for the love one feels for another man is quite a different sentiment from that of friendship which binds individuals to each other, since no one has
ever loved an ugly boy or an old man, no matter how well
preserved.

There never existed so many celibates as in the period of
Caesar and the first Roman emperors. It was also in this
epoch that pederasty was most evident. In any case, never
were Roman women so depraved as at this time.

Julius Caesar has often been accused of pederasty; it is
Suetonius who reports it. His first wars were waged in Asia.
Sent to Bithynia to bring back the fleet, he resided a long
time with King Nicomedes and it was this that instigated the
rumor of his practicing pederasty and of his prostituting himself for the king. This accusation was hurled at the con-
queror for a long time, and it caused many insults to be
heaped upon him by many people, Calvinus and Lucinius
among others. Curion, the elder, called him the Lupanar,

others, the queen of Bithynia. Cicero also says that Caesar
sacrificed the flower of his youth for Nicomedes. But as
Caesar was not particularly inimical to the feminine sex, he
could not protest against the words of Curion to the effect
that he was the husband of all the women and the wife of
all the men. According to Suetonius, he may also have had
sexual intercourse with Rufion, a freed slave. It is interesting to note here a habit of Caesar's which we shall return to
later in speaking of effeminisation. It caused him to adore
greatly the beauty of his body, to have his hair carefully cut
and to shave, and quite like the modern Uranist, he would
have his skin depilated, so that it might be as smooth as
possible.

Octavius, the first Roman Emperor and relative of Caesar.
also could not defend himself against the reputation of loving
men. He is supposed to have had sexual intercourse with
Caesar himself, and as Mark Anthony says, this was the price
of his adoption. During a theatrical representation, the expression of Cinoedus was reported by the people to the emperor. However, Suetonius believes that the later life of
Octavius positively belies these accusations.

Public opinion accuses Tiberius, the second emperor, of
pederasty in a far more positive manner (he was notorious
for his cruelty). Thus he had groups of girls and boys taken
to Capri where he conceived extreme subtleties in their sexual
relations. In his gardens he had special places reserved where
he incited young people of both sexes to immoral practices.
One day, in offering a sacrifice, he was so excited by looking
at a boy that he abused him immediately after the ceremony.

Caligula, Tiberius' successor, had the same reputation for
the abuse of natural functions. Besides certain nobles he held
as hostages in Rome, he had intercourse with Valerius Catullus. The latter seems to have contributed the most to the
reputation of Caligula, for he openly declared that the emperor impaired his health through his excesses.

Claudius was Caligula's successor on the Roman throne. It
is certain that during this reign pederasty was not unknown

Thus, during this period, Pompey, his son-in-law, was stabbed because he was found in the arms of a boy whom Claudius loved. The emperor Nero was also known for his excesses with boys. He had young Spotus changed into a woman by all possible artificial means and then married him heaping upon him honors due a Caesar's wife. As Nero was universally known and feared for his cruelty, it was regretted, they say, that his father had not married a woman such as he had chosen for himself. Be that as it may, Nero treated Spotus as an empress, embraced him openly and took him everywhere with him.

It may be said that Nero had a penchant for passive pederasty, and that he attached himself to a man named Doriphorus. It is true that Bruno Bauer considers a great number of facts imputed to Nero by Suetonius, Dio-Cassius and Aurelius Victor as pure inventions of his enemies. Dio-Cassius reproaches the philosopher Seneca, Nero's tutor, with having urged his pupil to practice pederasty.

According to Suetonius, the emperor Galba found more pleasure in intercourse with men than that with women. Besides, he preferred men who were thin and who were expert in immoral excesses. One day, he publicly and passionately embraced one of his lovers. His successor Othon was suspected of having had intercourse with Nero. In any case, he had feminine habits and had his skin depilated as Julius Caesar. The mild emperor Titus who was always surrounded by a great many eunuchs was also reputed for pederasty.

His successor, the emperor Domitian, appears to have had sexual relations with Clodius Pallio. A fact reported by Suetonius is otherwise interesting because it shows that however much depraved the customs during this period, Uranists were not considered exactly honorable by the Romans. In fact, a sedition having broken out during his reign, Domitian severely punished the principal offenders. Two of them were pardoned; it was shown that they were pederasts and that, because of this fact, they enjoyed the esteem neither of their peers nor of their soldiers, and consequently could have no influence over them. Nerva, Domitian's successor, was also a pederast. He is even said to have had sexual intercourse with his predecessor.

The subsequent Roman emperors were equally known for practicing pederasty. As characteristic of the customs of this period Ferdinand Gregoravius makes note of the fact that a man like Trajan used to make sacrifices to Love between Men.

In this respect, his successor Adrian occupies a unique place. His favorite was a young Greek of remarkable beauty, called Antinous, who it is said drowned himself in the Nile while Adrian was traveling in Egypt. He was, no doubt, the emperor's lover; many writers of fiction, such as George Taylor and O. Tinke have recounted tales in which he figured. But the motives which urged him on to suicide have not up to the present been decided. It is not known whether he sacrified himself of his own accord to avert a misfortune from the very superstitious Adrian, or whether the emperor had demanded the sacrifice of him. The opinions of ancient authors, such as Dio-Cassius, Spartianus and Aurelius Victor, are quite divided on this point. It is known, however, that Adrian revered the young man after his death, and according to Spartanius, mourned for him as for a woman. He had a city founded in Antinous' honor. It seems that in this case there existed a true reciprocated love. It is even supposed that Antinous committed suicide because of the jealousy caused by Adrian's fickleness. The dead Antinous was honored as a god by the emperor, who perhaps then only realized that he had lost a true love.

Heliogabulus was quite a pronounced Uranist. He dressed himself as a woman and gave the best positions to his lovers. Following the examples of Nero, he even wished to marry one of them. At the time of the mutinous outbreak which cost him his crown and his life, he wanted to fly with his lover, but he was killed by the soldiers. Tampidius said of the emperor Heliogabalus that he satisfied his lust on all parts

of the body. His love for Hiercoles the eunuch went so far
that he would kiss his genitals.

I have just reviewed a dynasty of Roman emperors known
for their pederasty and their Uranistic tastes. But it is evident, as we have already said, that these habits were not the
monopoly of the emperors, but were also shared by a great
many of their subjects. Besides, the poetry and other writings of this period are very positive in this respect.

Among the fables of Phaedrus the fifteenth entitled Prome-
theus (Book IV) refers quite clearly to Uranism among men:

> "He asked, what reason there,
>   The low prostitutes and gentle boys?
>   The old man replied."

The opposition between *tribades* and *molles mores* leaves no
doubt as to the fact that, under the name of "molles mores,"
reference is here made to men with feminine sensations who
feel an urge for sexual intercourse with other men. Besides,
the continuation of the fable fully confirms our supposition.
To the question put to him as to how Uranists and *tribades* were
created, the old man replied in words somewhat as follows:

> Promethius, who, according to certain ancient
> legends, created humankind, formed the bodies and
> the genital organs separately. When he was about
> to attach the genital organs to the bodies, he was in-
> vited to a feast by the god Bacchus. On his return,
> drunk and half asleep, Promethius mixed up the
> genital organs and applied to man those of women
> and to woman those of men. That is why the sexual
> urges was found inverted.

In Horace's poetry are to be found many passages relating
to love between men. In the Ode dedicated to Valgius,
Horace seeks to console him in the death of a boy whom he
loved. Valgius himself composed funeral chants on the death
of his beloved.

Horace himself was accused of pederasty because of many odes that he dedicated to men. But, no convincing proof of this fact is to be found on reading these odes. The most directly incriminating poetry includes absolutely nothing that can justify this assertion. The tenth ode of Book IV addressed to Ligurinus, contains, it is true, a few suspicious allusions: it describes Ligurinus as a handsome young man, whose beauty and youth, however, are destined to disappear later. Mantegazza counts Virgil also among the pederasts; under the name of Alexis he may have immortalized his love for the young Alexander. The second eclogue of Virgil is very important in so far as resolving the question.

Again we must cite Petronius' novel called "Satyricon" in which the author deals with pederasty and the customs during imperial Rome. Krafft-Ebing considers it the oldest novel having to do with pederasty. There is to be found also in the writings of the poets, in particular, of Martial, Juvenal, Catullus, etc., very important information bearing on our subject.

Tibullus who lived in a former period, also speaks without equivocation, in his "Elegies" of love for boys. He asks Priapus, son of Bacchus, how he obtained such good-looking boys. Priapus replies that he should not trust in the oaths of boys for they are perjurors in love. Masculine prostitution was very much widespread in Rome under the Caesars.

Besides the Greeks and the Romans, there were other ancient peoples who did not escape pederasty. Herodotus and Hipocrates have described a particular disease found among the Scythians; they dressed themselves as women and occupied themselves with all sorts of feminine affairs. According to Chevalier, Michae had already interpreted this disease as an aberration of the genital constitution. This is also the opinion of Krafft Ebing.

In Macedonia, love between men was likewise known. It is even said that Alexander the Great practiced it and that Hephestion was his favorite lover. Gregorovius likens the complaints of the great king on the death of Hephestion to those of Adrian mourning for Antinous.

According to certain authors love between men likewise existed among the ancient Teutons. Chevalier to whom we owe a great many historic indications bearing on our subject tells us that Diodorous determined the existence of pederasty among the ancient Gauls and the tribes of the Osques in Italy.

It is difficult to make an exact survey of sexual perversions during the Christian era, the middle ages and modern times up to the end of the eighteenth century.

But a great work of Paul Zacchias testifies to the fact that pederasty was widespread during these periods. According to Mantegazza, this phenomenon may have become diffused through France after the crusades. Philip the Good, prosecuted these practices with vigor, and it was during his reign that there occurred the celebrated trial of the Templars, who were accused of excessive abuses of natural functions. The first informer was Squin de Flexian, an old commander of the Order. However, it is not known to what point these accusations are founded. It is none the less interesting to note a usage which accompanied the reception of the neophytes. The candidate was obliged to embrace the one who received him "on an unusual or inconvenient part of the body, denuded for this purpose" and was thus held by modesty to keep it secret. Hen-Am Rhyn, from whom I borrow this detail, doubted the reality of this custom, while admitting that excesses must have been often practiced by the Templars. Later, the French accused Italians with having introduced pederasty into France.

The clergy and other members of the Catholic church were often made the object of the shameful reproach of pederasty. This is not at all astonishing, for the enemies of the church and the church itself hardly discriminated in its choice of the means of combat.

According to the "Aurea Monita" of the order of the Jesuits, the authenticity of which is even now doubtful, the sins of the flesh, particularly sodomy, were grounds for expulsion;

the superiors being exempted by the right of absolution.
Carl Julius Weber often reproaches them with the passion
for perverted love.   He also pictures for us the life as it was
led in the cloisters, towards the end of the XVIIIth century,
drawn from his own experiences.   In the convent at Eberach,
male sopranos took the place of boy singers in the choirs.
It was the favorite game of the monks to "play at marriage."
"This game," says Weber, "was perhaps inoffensive: let us,
through Christian charity, admit that it was so, since we have
never witnessed it.   But we should not forget *les regards de
faunes* that the monks, above all the Italians, cast on the good
looking boys whom they embraced as Jupiter must have embraced Ganymede and Socrates Alcibiades."   According to
Weber, it was the law of celibacy decreed by Hildebrand
(Gregory VII) that rapidly threw the Catholic clergy into
the most shameful debauches.   Although Hegel considers the
celibacy of the Catholic clergy as less counter nature than
good customs.   Nevertheless such an edict could favor the
development of love between men.

Besides, the works of a great many authors testify to the
fact that pederasty was quite widespread during the Middle
Ages.   Antonio Beccadelli, of Palmero (1394-1471) better
known as Panormitonus, has verbally maltreated the passions
that run counter to nature, in his "Hermaphrodite."   The
Orient also gives us several facts of love between men in the
Middle Ages.   During the reign of Constantine in Constanti-
nople men could be procured as easily as women.

Under Bajazett I (1389-1403) pederasty was widespread in
the Turkish Empire.   Visir Ali-paoha was very much attracted by Christian boys; he soon raised them to the rank
of pages, because of their beauty; therein lay the beginning,
or, more justly in my mind, the open manifestation of pederasty in the Ottoman empire.   Many wars against the Chris-
tians may have had no other purpose than to procure Chris-
tion youths for the Turkish debauches and to fill spaces left
empty in the ranks of the pages.   Greek, Serbian, Bulgarian
and Hungarian youths surrendered themselves to the passions

of their masters, often to get less vicious employment. The order given by the grand vizir, towards the end of April, 1771, at the beginning of a campaign to chase all the "youngsters" out of the camp, is characteristic of the way in which pederasty was openly practiced in the Near-East until modern times. Furthermore, this order was not executed. The Musulmans have often been accused of immorality, as much because of the existence of pederasty as of harems and of other analogous institutions among them. However, Muller who has great knowledge of the subject believes that immorality is very much rarer among the Musulmans than it is among the peoples of the Occident.

A great many eastern poets, Turkish and Persian, have sung of love between men. Hoessli has brought together in his book a great many poems and communications on this theme. I borrow most of my facts from him. The Turkish poet Ruscheni had as his lawyer a good looking young man named Chysr. Ssaadi Tschelebi, the sage, noted for his virtue, has left us a whole series of poems, among others, the following verses addressed to a youth:

> The fair moon of thy beauty lights the world;
> Thy dark eyes cause me to lose my reason, etc.

Ssaki, the renowed calligrapher, was also known as having relations with an attractive boy to whom he may have given his entire fortune. In Persia we see the poets often celebrating the love between men in verse. The Persian poet Sadi is the author of many poems in which he supplicates his lover. After the death of his well beloved, Sadi laments:

> "May my eyes no longer see the world in which my lover no longer exists; would I were lying with thee under the earth on which my head now reclines, moistening thy tomb with my tears—"

At the moment of parting with the man he loves, he cries:

> "Bitter-sweet is the goodbye kiss on the lips of my friend," etc.

The fact that Sadi lived about the year 1300 gives particular importance to his erotic poetry. The poet seeks to introduce a moral element into all his poems dealing with love between men. Thus he asks, "How is it that a king sometimes loves the least attractive of a number of boys of looks ranging to the most attractive? In such love is found the answer: what charms the heart likewise charms the eyes." We have also to mention Hafiz, who died in 1394, one of the greatest Persian poets. Most of his poems are addressed to his lovers, with whom he had physical contact; there is no doubt that the following deals with love between men:

> "If the lovely cup-bearer finds favor in my eyes, I would sweep the grounds of his dwelling with the lashes thereof."
> "The wind gently played with the curls of his hair, and the world cast its shadow of jealousy upon me."
> "Oh, well beloved! The light of the moon shines on thy face and the dimple in thy chin hides a well of passions!—May it always be my great good fortune to kiss thy honeyed lips."

Another well known Persian poet, Mewlaua Dscheleleddin Rumi, who died in 1273, has likewise left us, among his other works, some poetry referring to pederasty, several lines of which follow:

> The rose of love is the symbol supreme,
> To the friend of my bosom, to give it I dream.
> —In its heart a thorn in silence is borne,
> For never is love of pain quite shorn.

The Persian poet preferred to sing of the cup-bearer:

> My eye finds rest in the sight of the cup-bearer,
> My ear in the sound of the lute—
> Come, cup-bearer, for I would very much like to
>   serve thee—

In the preceding pages, I have studied the manifestations of love between men, from the most ancient times up to the end of the eighteenth century. We have seen that in the West pederasty was regarded as a vice, while in the Near-East it enjoyed greater consideration. Western literature furnishes us only rarely with scientific facts in regard to the question, and it is only towards the end of the eighteenth century that these facts began to be studied in a more rational way. However, let us add that, even before this period, mention is already made of the existence of the phenomena under consideration. In this regard, may be cited Boccaccio, Machiavelli, Aretinus, Casanova, in his Memoirs, Voltaire in his "Socratic Love" (in his "Philosophic Dictionary"). In recent years, the scientific side of the question has been brought more to light; for example, by Wieland, or again, by Herman Klencke, in his "System of Organic Psychology," and by many others. Instead of speaking of homosexual love, Klencke speaks of Pythagorian love. I believe this a misnomer, for I have found nothing that could justify this term, so far as Pythagorus or his disciples are concerned. Randohr and Meiners have done most to place this problem on a truly scientific basis. Homosexuality is studied in detail in "Venus Urania" and the works of Ramsdohr.

Randohr expresses himself very clearly on the question of love between men, showing great insight and an extensive experience. Not only does he examine in detail the opinions of the Ancient Greeks and of other peoples on the question of pederasty, but he also informs us of the frequency of Uranism during his period (at the end of the eighteenth century). He does not admit that sexual accord ought to exist only between two beings capable of contributing to the propagation of the species. According to him, the sexual urge can manifest itself in two individuals belonging to the same sex.

In Moritz' "Magazin Fur Erfahrungssee Lekund" we find two cases which are clearly those of sexual perversion. Although, in these observations, pederasty is strongly disputed in the two cases, quite a decided urge towards men is none the less found in them. In one of them, sexual perversion did not appear, at least in all its vigor until the subject had made the acquaintance of another man. This peculiarity is, among other things, well known, and sexual perversion does not infrequently remain dormant for quite a while and then manifest itself only on the occasion of an encounter with a certain individual.

Randohr points out an author named Hoessli who, in 1836, launched an impassioned campaign, in which he attempts to justify the love between men. His book, called "Eros," which we have already cited, is in two volumes; despite its great length, which makes its reading difficult, it contains very valuable material from a biographical point of view.

At that time, there occurred a very interesting court trial in Switzerland. A man of a very sympathetic nature had for unknown cause killed a young man. He was consequently condemned to die. Hoessli, who believed that the case had to do with an assassination motivated by jealousy, went to great pains in trying to solve the mystery. He succeeded in getting Zschocke to write a novel in which a young girl, disguised as a youth, succeeded in kindling the flame of love for her in the breast of a certain man. But it is evident that the celebrated novelist did not understand Hoessli's intention. In 1844, Kaan published a work (Psychopathia Sexualis) in which he studied pederasty and onanism, but more particularly the latter.

In 1847, Brierre de Boismont, Michea and other authors pointed out several cases of sexual perversion in France. In 1849 Michea attracted attention to homosexual love in a case of necrophilia. In 1852 Casper wrote several articles in his journal on pederasty. He insists principally on the fact that this state is often congenital, and that the desires concerned are not always satisfied by the *immissio in anum*. Besides, he points out that it is sometimes due to manifestations arising from decadent customs. At the same time, Casper gives a whole list of very interesting documents and biographies of

Uranists. A case of pederasty in which Casper figured as an expert, caused a great sensation. The principal defendant was a Count whom Casper calls Count "Cains." The same author has also embodied certain materials in his "Clinical Novels." About the same time in France Tardieu published a work on pederasty. He appears to have acquired much experience in this phase of the subject and to have examined a considerable number of facts.

Besides the authors whose work we have briefly mentioned, we should also cite Schopenhauer who likewise was familiar with sexual perversions. It is known that in the mind of this philosopher everything in the world has a determined goal. According to him this goal exists also for sexual perversions as practiced by old men. As these generally procreate feeble offspring, nature has given them an urge, not for women, but for men, so as to offset the physical degeneration of human kind. Also in his book "The World as Will and as Idea" he finds in pederasty hardly anything but advantages.

About 1860, attention was attracted to an author who published a series of works on sexual perversions, at first under the pseudonymo of "Numa Numantius," then under his own name of Carl Heinrichs Ulrichs. He was a State Assessor who had acquired a certain reputation through other works. As we have said in the preceding chapter, we are indebted to him for the scientific term of Uranist. His purposes in writing are the study of Uranism and its justification. Noteworthy, was his plea for the abrogation of all the articles of the law which dealt with love between men. According to him this love should be as free as the love between man and woman, and the law should intervene in the former only under the same condition that it would in the latter. Ulrichs' works are remarkable from a number of viewpoints. As Chevalier puts it, he has been the only one for many years to study the problem of sexual perversions scientifically. It is certain that he goes much too far in his conclusions. Thus he asks that marriage between men be authorized similarly to marriage between man and woman! If he had not expressed his opinion so ardently, he would certainly have served the cause he defended better than he had. As he was himself a Uranist according to his own confession he speaks, in a way, *pro domo sua* and allows himself such liberties of expression as are hard at times to consider scientific. In 1865 at the Congress of German Law in Graz, Ulrichs, together with Professor Tewes, asked for the abrogation in all the German states of the articles in the Penal Code referring to love between men. In 1867 he again took up the same question at the Congress of Munich and it seems that it was expressly tabled to avoid a scandal. In 1870 a German editor wanted to publish a periodical entitled "Uranus" having to do only with the problems of sexual perversions. But it seems that only the first number appeared; at least, I have not seen any others.

A little while before, Griesinger, one of the most eminent German psychiatrists, dealt with the problem of Uranism in the first of a course of lectures which he delivered in 1869 in the psychiatric clinic in Berlin. This lecture however does not appear to have been very interesting. In 1869 M. Frankel of Dessau in a communication devoted to sexual perversions among pederasts mentions among other things, hallucinations and other psychic troubles. A little while after, a new impulse was given to the controversy by Westphal who as we have already seen introduced into science the term sexual inversions to designate the phenomenon under consideration. In his opinion it is a congenital disease. At first he publishes two cases, insisting above all on the fact that the patients were quite conscious of the morbid character of their condition.

Westphal's publication was followed in Germany by a certain number of works on the problem confronting us. These works appeared almost exclusively in the "Archiv für Psychiatrie" edited by Westphal. Among these authors we can here cite: Scholz, Gock, Schminke, Luman, Sterz, Krug, Rabow, Blumer, Savage, Servaes and others. Bastiew observes that sexual perversion is not rare among non-civilized peoples; that among them, the sexual perverts are considered as superior beings, as saints, and form a sort of exclusive caste. Krafft-Ebing's book on sexual psychopathology, which appeared in 1891, contains a more extensive bibliography of the subject. In 1876, at the Congress of the Alienists of Southern Germany, Stark made an important contribution to the subject, based on a great many new observations. Since that time, publications have multiplied in Germany as well as in other counrties. One of the most remarkable cases was published by Charcot and Magnan. In 1885, Magnan published his work on sexual perversion, a little while after Lacassagne of Lyons delivered lectures on the same subject. In France this phenomenon was called the inversion of the sexual instinct. So also did Charcot and Magnan and this term was likewise used by a certain number of Italian authors.

In 1886 Tarnowsky published a book containing a great many contributions to the subject of perversion and sexual aberrations. What this book lacks is a systematic classification and a sufficiently clear differentiation between the various forms of sexual perversion.

We have again expressly mentioned in passing an author who during a great many years has contributed the most to the study of this problem: namely, Krafft-Ebing. As early as 1877 he published a rather complete study of sexual perversion. In 1881, he published a more extended work on the same subject. But it is above all his "Psychopathia Sexualis" that constitutes a systematic monograph on sexual perversion. By successive additions this book was transformed in several years into a more considerable work, the last edition of which appeared in 1891. It was Krafft-Ebing who attempted a precise classification of the different forms of sexual perversion. It was he who ascertained the existence of certain varieties of sexual aberrations, such as masochism, sadism, fetichism, while showing the relations which existed between them and sexual inversion, properly so called: But what gives an entirely unique value and importance to Krafft-Ebing's work is the inclusion of a certain number of sincere autobiographies of patients, which have considerably enriched this scientific field.

There is no doubt that pederasty and Uranism are to be found not only among the civilized peoples of the North but also in other countries. In certain regions along the Mediterranean masculine prostitution unmistakably exists even today. In Naples during the evening youths offer themselves to passers-by on the *via Toledo,* and the panders praise their masculine as well as their feminine charms. We have proof of the fact that Uranism has always been more widespread in Italy than in any other country of Europe. Ramsdohr is responsible for the opinion that love between men was not at all infrequent in Italy during the eighteenth century. We also possess numerous facts relating to pederasty in the Orient. Heinrich von Baltzahn relates in one of his books that in the suburbs of Kaaba youths offer themselves to strangers. Another traveler tells us that in Cairo while he was bargaining for two slaves, the merchant said to him, "You count for nothing the pleasure they will bring you!" Lenz mentions in his book of travel entitled "Timbuctoo," the immorality of the important personages of the empire who had young castrated negroes in their possession. These are taken from among the children of their slaves; the custom is so general that no one pays heed to it any longer and only Europeans are astonished at the openness with which it is spoken and treated.

According to Krauss pederasty is even today very widespread in China. He further states that the city of Tschang-Theu teems with panders for pederasts who are known as catamites. In the country this role is ordinarily played by slaves. In Pekin they form a class by themselves. There exists in that city certain houses where boys of eleven to twelve years are brought up for prostitution. At the theatres may be seen honorable citizens having with them their "Amosu," that is to say, their favorite lovers. The sensual orgies which take place there can hardly be compared with any but those of ancient Rome. A person who has lived a long time in Japan and who is well acquainted with its customs and habits, has told us that it is to be met with frequently in that country. It seems to exist principally among pupils in boarding schools and among soldiers in barracks. However pederasty is not practiced so openly in Japan as it is in China.

Tarkowsky says that the fame and riches of the Musulman are measured by the number of boys he has in his service. The facts relative to pederasty in the Orient and in Africa are very numerous. The same phenomena may be observed not only in the Orient but also in many other foreign regions. Mantegazza, from whom I borrow a great many details, gives us very valuable information on the subject in his "Anthropological Studies of Love Between Men." He states that in certain parts of Mexico there were times when even marriage existed between men. Communications of travelers on the existence of pederasty in California and in Nicaragua are very positive. Mantegazza goes on to relate how when America was discovered pederasts were found among the inhabitants of Panama. This fact proves the existence of pederasty among primitive peoples. All our studies of the peoples of America indicate that pederasty existed there before the arrival of Europeans; the same is true of Peru. In Madagascar there were male dancers who dressed as women and practiced pederasty. According to an article by Westphal the same phenomenon existed among the Indians. Among us there is a class of men who cannot resist the temptation to dress as women and to conduct themselves actually like women. Furthermore Virey in his "Natural History of Mankind" recounts that sexual intercourse between men existed among the Indians in North America.

Hammond reports an analagous fact among the descendants of the Aztecs of New Mexico. Each branch of its families would furnish under the name of "Mujerado" one of their members for the religious rites in which pederasty played an important part. The "mujerado" received a special education. Through masturbation and continual horseback riding a paralytic impotence was induced in him. In this way was obtained an atrophy of the penis and the testicles, and an effeminization analogous to that of eunuchs. The hair of the beard fell out, the voice became higher in pitch, so that in the last analysis, the mujerado showed feminine tendencies and took his place wholly in the ranks of women.

I will now review a series of individuals of the eighteenth century accused of sexual perversion. Far be it from me that by these studies I should besmirch the names of these persons. The spirit in which I conceived this book shows that if I admit the existence of sexual perversion in any individual I consider it as purely pathologic, and in no way affecting their character. Gley was right in saying that in this respect one must be very prudent in interpreting historical facts. It is easy to pass an opinion but it is not always easy to prove it. In any case one must not use the methods of Moreau, Ulrichs and others, who completely neglect to uphold their assertions relative to the existence of sexual perversions in some person by sufficient proof. But I have no reason to neglect completely the indications I possess of Uranism in certain persons of historic importance. Such an attitude would likewise be incompatible and would militate against the complete understanding of the problem. Unfortunately in the biographies of these people almost all that pertains to the sexual life is suppressed especially in the case of the existence of sexual perversion. However I have been able to find in biographies and historical works many facts which later directly indicate the existence of sexual perversion in these people, or simply show the presence of feminine tendencies.

Henry III, king of France who reigned from 1574 to 1589 is considered not without reason as a Uranist. It is interesting to note that Charles XI (1560-1574), the predecessor of Henry III, was also accused of pederasty. As we have already said the French attributed to Catherine de Medici, the mother of these two kings, the introduction of pederastic habits into France. D'Aubiguq has furnished us with very

concise details on the subject of Henry III and pederasty.
In almost all historical treatises facts may be found which
leave hardly a doubt. The king was surrounded by a great
many favorites, who were called "mignons," whose effeminacy
was universally known. In the king's palace balls and festi-
vals were held in which the feminine element was not lacking. The king loved to appear in public dressed as a woman.
He did not in the least hide his love for his "mignons" from
the eyes of the world. The king also had sadistic tendencies,
proof of which is found in his passion for whipping his "mignons" on days of penitence. Sadism is a combination of cruelty
and sexual ideas: we shall return to it later. Krafft-Ebing has
drawn attention to the connection between the "flagellants"
(in the Middle Ages and later) who whipped themselves as
a sign of penitence, and the sexual urges which, in certain
pathological conditions, are awakened by whipping. It is precisely during Henry the Third's reign that the "flagellants"
were very numerous in Paris. In a picture which appeared
shortly after his death, the king is represented in military
costume but with his hair curled like a woman's and with
several articles belonging to a woman's toilette.

Edward II of England (1307-1327) also had the reputation
of being a Uranist. He found the pleasure and diversions of
court life much to his liking, and he had his favorite raised
to the highest positions. Peter Gaveston was his special
favorite. He knew how to attach himself to the king "by
seductive bonds." After Gaveston's death the king's favors
went to Hugo Spenser. The king was finally dethroned and
the queen who had deserted him absolutely refused a recon-
ciliation. In passing, we may mention the fact that the king
was extraordinarily loquacious and that he could not guard
even State secrets.

James I of England (1603-1625) son of Mary Stuart, known
also as James VI of Scotland is regarded by Uranists as one
of their number. More rightly, it seems to me, than in the
case of Edward II. There were decidedly abnormal traits in
James' character: the love of absolutism, coupled with cow-

ardice, and weakness of character; interest in science as well as infantile pedantry. His lack of poise has been described as also the absence of virility in his general appearance. Although he was married to a Danish princess by whom he had several children, that fact did not lessen his bad reputation caused by the domination exercised over him by his favorites. It was George Villiers, duke of Buckingham, who found especial favor in the king's eyes, because of his physical beauty. He exercised a considerable influence on the government of the country. Through his affection for unworthy favorites, the king succeeded in awakening a feeling of discontent in his people. He had formerly reigned in Scotland as James VI and neither was he able there to hide his weakness for youths of imposing appearance. He attracted them to him so that in his service they came to exercise a great influence on the country. There were two men called Arren and Lennox who veritably dominated the king.

A very curious personality is that of Rudolph II of Hapsburg, who reigned over Germany from 1576 to 1612. He fell more and more into an apathetic state, and had neither energy nor force of character. He was the victim of caprices and fantasies of all sorts. In his Hradschin museum he amassed a great number of natural and artistic curiosities, books, precious stones and antiques. The emperor passed much time in his gardens and his stables, but he had a sickly exaggerated idea of the importance of his duties. His favorites really exercised the authority. His personal valets, highly immoral men, were important personages, without whom it was impossible to obtain anything. It was with these unworthy creatures that princes and statesmen had to deal. Later, the king showed no uncertain sign of moral perversion. Thus, Veber paints, in his "Universal History" the character of this king. If I add that according to Ireland, he hated women, it could be concluded that his love for his favorites had a sexual basis. Without doubt, we are told, on the other hand, that this king, who had no legitimate children, left a great many bastards, but we lack exact details on the latter. What is more, information about the women with whom he had intimate relations is not forthcoming, while the names of his favorites are well known.   Ireland, furthermore, compares Rudolph II with Louis II of Bavaria, of whom we shall speak later, and he find in them a common aversion for women.

We find in the life of Pope Paul II (1464-1471) a truly curious phenomenon.   An unbounded vanity was at the root of his character.   While Cardinal he proposed to assume the name of Formosus if he was elected pope, because of his physical beauty.   His sacerdotal robes were lined with gold and sparkled with diamonds.   He cried on the slightest provocation and must have had a veritable passion for collecting precious stones.   He never showed himself in public without adornments of some sort.   Because of the ease with which his tears flowed he was called "My Lady of Pity."   I do not find that he was formally considered a Uranist; but I believe it my duty to cite his case here because of his effeminate traits which may often exist without a Uranistic tendency. Furthermore this pope may have left a daughter.

There is no doubt that Pope Sixtus IV (1471-1484) Paul's successor, had the habits of a Uranist.   Weber believes that a great many of his favorites were elevated to the dignity of cardinal.   Certain cardinals may have even asked permission of the pope to practice sodomy during the warm season and this request was favorably received.   It is in reference to this pope that Weber quotes the following verses:

Since Rome (Roma) delighted in inverse love (amor)
Love took its name from inverse Rome.

It is also interesting to note Sixtus' cruelty and his love for bloody spectacles.   He had an especial desire to witness duels fought under his windows.   Among historical personages who have been accused of pederasty I may also mention Pope Julius II (1503-1573).   Geiger does not think that this accusation upheld by the contemporaries of the pope is well

founded, although, according to the same author, his character and manners were not without suspicion. Julius II may
have been one of the cardinals who asked permission of Pope
Sixtus IV to practice pederasty during the warm season.

Michael Angelo Buonarotti, the great sculptor, contemporary of Pope Julius II who made him come to Rome, is likewise accused of sexual perversion, and, we believe, not without reason. We may be sure of one thing, and that is that
the love for woman does not figure in the life of this great
artist. Without doubt, when a woman with whom he may
have had relations is sought, Vittoria Colonna is often mention. Grimm, Michael Angelo's biographer, believes that their
relations were simply of friendship and that love entered not
at all. When he knew the princess both were no longer
young, and Vittoria Colonna was never anything but the
"princess" for him. In the sculptor's poetry passages are to
be found which have been instanced as proof of his love for
women. But here again the existence of love for women
should not be deduced solely from poems addressed to
women, especially when the woman of whom the poet sings
is not known. Even poetry consecrated to love between men
does not imply the existence of Uranism in the poet, if the
poetry is not dedicated or consecrated to a male, whose identity may be determined. The relations of Michael Angelo
with Tommaso de Cavalieri appear to me not above suspicion.
The latter was a young painter of noble birth and remarkably
good looks, who could have of Michael Angelo all he wished.
The relations between Michael Angelo already old, and young
Cavalieri must have been very intimate, and I do not believe
that the bonds which united them were simply those of friendship. They may be judged by the following lines addressed
to Cavalieri by Michael Angelo:

> I see a soft light with thine eyes:
> I am blind for my eyes they see not.
> In keeping pace with thee,
> The weight of my burden is lightened.

Carried away on thy wings,
I fly with thee to heaven.
As thou wishest: I feel bold or I tremble,
Being cold in summer, warm in the days of winter.

In thy will reposes mine,
In thy heart my thoughts are born,
In thy spirit the source of my words is found.

E'en thus I am like to the moon
Which we see in the sky
Only when by the sun illumined with rays of fire.

This sonnet, addressed to Cavalieri, is not the expression of a love that is solely sensual. Neither is it dictated, as it seems to me, by a sentiment purely that of friendship. In it is found a spirit which recalls that of Socrates in Plato's "Banquet." Moreover, Grimm compares the intercourse between Michael Angelo and Cavalieri with that which existed between Socrates and Alcibiades. Springer believes that Michael Angelo evinced a friendship forced to a passionate extreme and analogous to that which Winkelmann later succumbed. A letter from Cavalieri to Michael Angelo, in our possession, indicates more than a mere friendship: its language is rather that of a "pampered favorite."

Giovanni Antonio Razzi (1479-1564), one of the most celebrated Italian painters, a contemporary of Pope Leo X, was notorious for his life of debauchery and vice which caused him to receive the surname of "il Sodoma" by which he is even today designated in a number of works. Leo X, himself not of very rigorous morals (being even accused of pederasty) had the painter raised to the dignity of cavalier. Then again Fiorillo says that the thoughtlessness and debauchery which led the painter to his reckless mode of life partly reflects itself in his painting. Razzi, whose painting consists mostly of frescoes, is not well known outside of Italy; but the Italians consider him one of the most eminent of painters and place him beside Leonardo da Vinci. Vischer, another biographer, says that the work of Razzi is greatly marred by a "lack of virility," his manner being too "effeminate."

Muret, the well-known historian, lived from 1526 to 1585. The facts relative to perverse tendencies in the great savant are furnished me by Foisset. His attempt to exonerate Muret from homosexual activities do not seem to me very convincing. The facts of Muret's life leave no doubt that his sexual life was abnormal. In 1552 Muret lectured on philosophy and civil law in Paris and his course attracted a considerable number of pupils. At this time he was accused of unnatural practices and imprisoned in Chatelet where in despair he went on a hunger strike. His friends obtained his freedom. He then went to Toulouse where he lectured on Roman law. There also he was accused of sexual immorality and condemned to be burned with his accomplice, a young man named Luc-Menge-Fremiot, as a sodomist according to the law of 1554. Muret succeeded in fleeing to Italy where the same accusation was brought against him in several cities notably in Venice and in Padua. Despite these accusations he succeeded thanks to his services to science, to make the acquaintance of eminent Italians.

Nor did Shakespeare escape the accusation of having sexual relations with men. As proofs of his assertion certain of his sonnets are cited which, although addressed to a man (probably the Duke of Southampton) speaks the language of love. Bodenstedt formally maintains that in the sonnets in question there are no intimations of love between men, as Barnstorff pretends in his "Key to the Sonnets of Shakespeare." The most incriminating sonnet is the following:

A woman's face with nature's own hand painted
Hast thou, the master-mistress of my passion,
A woman's gentle heart, but not acquainted
With shifting change, as is false woman's fashion;
An eye more bright than their's, less false in rolling,
Gilding the object whereupon it gazeth.

Of man in hue, all fused in his controlling,
Which steals men's eyes and women's soul amazeth.
And for a woman were thou first created
Till Nature, as she wrought thee fell a-doting,
And by addition me of thee defeated,
By adding one thing, to my purpose nothing.
But since she trick'd thee out for women's pleasure
Mine by thy love, and thy love's youth their treasure.

Bodenstedt attributes the amorous tone of this sonnet
(and also of others) to the fact that during Shakespeare's
time there existed a veritable cult of friendship between men,
thanks to which, the tenderest expressions of love were employed in references to friendship. He believes that this state
of affairs was brought about by the powerful influence of the
Greek and Latin poets on the Elizabethans.

Johann Joachim Winckelmann (1717-1768), the great critic,
was accused more than once of Uranism. As proof of this
letters have been cited in which this passion is expressed in
no mistaken terms. Justi, a biographer who attempts to deny
it, is himself obliged to admit that the letters of Winckelmann often bear witness to a certain amount of sensuality.
I am convinced that if letters such as those of Winckelmann's
were addressed to a woman, no one would deny the existence
of amorous relations between the correspondents. If we admit that love between men exists, we are obliged to admit
the expressions of love in Winckelmann's letters, especially
since nothing in his life tends to belie this supposition.
Johann Friedrich Vagt, editor of these letters, expressed himself, in his preface, in the following manner: "These letters
describe the attitude of mind and the sensations of Winckelmann very well; they should be well known before one con-
templates writing his biography—." These letters are addressed to the lawyer, Friedrich Reinhold von Berg of Tivo-
nia. His friendship for Berg dated from their first meeting.
The great artist said to Berg, "I have found in you a beautiful body, a soul created for virtue; the day when I am sepa-

rated from you shall be the most sorrowful day of my life."
Whoever reads these letters cannot but agree with us in our
opinion of Winckelmann. In the letter dated June 9th, 1762,
Winckelmann writes, "As a solicitous mother inconsolably
mourns her beloved child, so, my sweet friend, I deplore our
separation with all my heart." In his letter of the 10th of
February, 1764, addressed to Berg, Winckelmann begins by
calling him "My well beloved and very beautiful friend" and continues with, "All the names I could call you are not tender
enough and do not express the fulness of my love—. I embrace your image and I die. Your eternally devoted friend
and your obedient servant, Winckelmann."

The murder of Winckelmann at the inn at Trieste sustains
with a fair degree of certainty the opinion that he was a
Uranist. There is no doubt that Winckelmann knew his murderer Arcangeli for only a short time before his death; the
latter dogged his steps to Trieste. They were so bound to
each other, that they seemed to have been friends for many
years. It is a known fact that the murderer was a dilettante,
entirely devoid of culture, and without the slightest intellectual interest for the great critic.

According to certain opinions the murderer succeeded in cap-
turing the entire confidence of Winckelmann by posing as a
man of artistic tastes and by simulating quite an unusual
attachment for him. He had been a cook, previously condemned to death, and subsequently pardoned. It may be admitted, as Jordens thinks that such an individual may have
been able to pass successfully in the eyes of a critic such as
Winckelmann as a connoisseur of art. Theft was admitted
as the motive of the crime and Arcangeli was executed.

Prince Henry, brother of Frederick the Great, was also accused of pederasty. In "The Secret History of the Court of
Berlin" in which the "Letters of a French Traveler" (Mira-
beau) appeared in 1786-1787 there are to be found very convincing passages. One reads: "An old servant of Prince
Henry's apt in serving his master's passion for pederasty, became his favorite at first, and was then made canon of Mag-

debourg where the prince was bishop" . . . "The aristocracy of the army knows that with Prince Henry the Gany-
medes have always made and shall always make the decisions." From other sources come indications of the pederastic tendencies of Prince Henry. There is no doubt that his
relations with his wife were very tenuous, that they lived
separately, and that when he met her at court, he did not
speak to her.

If I rely on certain oral communications, the poet Byron
may have also been held to be a Uranist. However, nothing
in his life or works indicates that the accusation is well
founded. It may be based on the fact that the poet was often
accompanned by a young girl dressed as a boy. Moreover
this reputation is perhaps due to the calumnies to which the
great poet was exposed during his whole life.

Among poets suspected of the practice of pederasty, one
must also name Count Platen whose contemporaries seem
rather united in recognizing the fact. The poetry which he
dedicated to men, and in which he sings of friends and cup-
bearers (Jupiter and Ganymede, the great classic example),
must have contributed much towards creating such a reputation for him. But, on the other hand, it is maintained that
Platen was inspired in his poetry by the characteristics of
Oriental poetry. The fact of his having addressed love poems
to women has not changed the reputation he acquired of
lover of men.

Platen one day found himself involved in a heated literary
controversy with Heine whom he reproached with his Jewish
origin. Heine took vengeance on the aristocratic poet by ac-
cusing him publicly of pederasty. In his "Baths of Lucullus."
there are many passages relative to this question. Therein
Heine speaks of the warmly fraternal friendship of Count
Platen who addresses to "A Man" and not to "A Woman"
poems in which he expresses his sentiments, exhaling an odor
quite different from that of eau de Cologne, in which the
amorous dalliances are immoral and seems to be written by
a girl. He compares him to Nero who married a boy, and

calls him "man of the behind" and not "man of the head."
This polemic between the two poets made a great stir in Germany. Strodtmann himself, Heine's biographer, does not approve of the means employed by Heine in the verbal combat.
At any rate there is no doubt that it has done much to hurt
Heine. In a letter addressed to Varnhagen, Heine treats
Platen as an insolent youth who prostitutes himself to the
aristocracy and the clergy. Besides, before Heine's attack,
Count Platen was already pulled to pieces by Ludwig Robert
because of the themes of his poetry. At first, Platen intended
to sue Heine but he forbore to do so, because Heine could
have furnished the proof of his allegations.

In closing, we shall cite one of the incriminating poems of
Platen's:

> Thou hast caused me many a cruel hour,
> But let heaven forefend lest it take vengeance on thee,
> For, otherwise, tears in streams down my cheeks had
>   flowed,
> When thou hadst pronounced my name.
>
> While dispelling betimes all illusions,
>   e'en into truth the issue forcing,
> I would like—and I do it through weakness
> To defend thee, my friend! For I am not troubled
> By superficial arguments.
>
> It is true that I could hardly protect thee;
> But serve thee of mine eyes
> To plead thy cause for thee.
>
> In measure as they, in seeking thine,
>   meet glance for glance,
> So shall they find therein such sustenance
>   as to them for love is needful
> But thou, read in their gaze my suffering.

Among historic personages manifestly of Uranistic tendencies, let me also mention Louis II, the unhappy king of Bavaria. There is no doubt that he was violently given to sexual inversion. The details which follow were borrowed from the brochure of Ireland, "Power and Madness," based on a great many works and containing a psychological study of this king. Even before Louis II's madness was officially declared he appears to have manifested symptoms of sexual inversion. His coldness and even his aversion for women were well known, and these were manifestly repeated on many occasions. He would write very tender letters to men, more tender than those which fiancés exchange between themselves. No doubt much has been said of his love for men but this point has always been treated with silence by those who were competent to speak, a fact which constitutes an argument, according to Ireland, in favor of the Uranistic tendencies of the king. It is in this fact that we should seek the interpretation of the cruel treatment he inflicted on certain persons of his retinue; and it is this fact which is explained by the instinct of cruelty common to all Sadists. During the last years of his life, Louis II always took great pleasure in the suffering and torture which he inflicted on others. It appears that the psychic love that the king manifested for certain persons of the masculine sex was entirely independent of the physical satisfaction found in the sexual act.

One could further enlarge this chapter on historic Uranists, among whom certain authors also include Charles VII of Sweden, William of Orange, and a certain number of other persons who played a role in history. I prefer to stop here, and to report no more than one case dating from the seventeenth century and having a general significance, in the sense that as in many actual cases, it is impossible of explanation without admitting the existence of sexual inversion.

Many murders and suicides whose cause escape us are to be attributed to this disease. A case in question caused a great stir in its time and is reported in "Secret Histories and

Mysterious Men" by Friedrich Bulau. It has to do with the murder of Henry Gottlob von Debschitz, aged thirty-five, at Languenau, in 1692. The victim's family belonged to the nobility in the region. Nowhere is it said that the love for men played a role in this affair. But how is one to explain this mystery otherwise when it is known that the assassin, Braun von Merzdorf, had stabbed his victim, whom he saw for the first time, after having embraced and caressed him in his bed? It is evident that von Debschitz must have repulsed his caresses. The influence of jealousy, violently and brusquely awakened, suffices to explain the murder.

Chapter III

SOCIAL STUDY

Ratio of Inverts; Anatomy of Inverts; Feminization; Elise Edwards; Clothes and the Pervert; Voice, Walk, and Work; Habits of the Invert; Inverts, Jealousy and Vanity, etc.; Effeminate Traits; Male Prostitution; Married Inverts; Inverts and Women; Parties and Balls; Names Given to Inverts.

It is impossible to estimate the exact number of Uranists or their ratio to the entire population. Even the authorities cannot give us precise information on this point, for they come in contact only with those Uranists who are accused of committing misdemeanors. The majority remain quite unknown and entirely escape the police and the courts. According to the statistics of different sources there may be nearly 4,000 men who sell themselves. I believe this number is exaggerated. I can say, however, that in Berlin, I personally know of 300 to 400 Uranists and I have heard 100 to 200 others mentioned. According to these figures I am sure that there are 500 Uranists, *at least,* in Berlin. I find it impossible to say whether there are in Berlin 3,000 or 10,000 Uranists, or even more. This uncertainty of statistics arises from the fact that a great many inverted individuals escape all notice, even medical care.

In certain cities the Uranists themselves estimate the number of their fellows. Thus a Uranist told me that in Magdeburg, he knew 70; but the number is probably greater than that. I find it difficult to say whether Uranism is more widespread in the large cities than in the small, or whether more so in the country than in the city. The greater number of patients who have been scientifically observed have lived in cities for a length of time. It does not at all arise from this that their passion was the result of bad example. Krafft-Ebing also gives us some information as to the number of Uranists in certain cities. One of his patients told him that he knew 14 Uranists in a city of 13,000 inhabitants, and 80 in another, with a population of 60,000. Krafft-Ebing does not doubt the sincerity of his patient, but he believes that he does not sufficiently differentiate between congenital and acquired Uranism.

According to Ulrichs 25,000 adult Uranists were living in Prussia. As an average, he counts one Uranist to 2,000 inhabitants or 500 men. Ulrichs himself was a Uranist and all his writings reflect the fact, but it is evident that, so far as the number of Uranists is concerned, he should have tended to diminish rather than to exaggerate it.

In a general way, one must not take literally all that the Uranist relate on the subject. A great many of them tend to exaggerate the figures involved. I know some, who, among three persons and even two, always find a Uranist and tell fantastic tales about their sexual relations.

As in the case of the love of man for woman, sexual inversion is the privilege of no single class and is found in all levels of society. However, it is my general impression that inversion is more frequently found among the members of the higher levels of society. This is not at all surprising when one considers that the predisposition to nervousness is a very favorable condition for the development of sexual perversion and that this predisposition exists largely among the members of the cultured class. Mantegazza rightfully insists on the fact that Uranism is found not only in the dregs of society but more often among individuals reputed for their learning and high social position.

The Uranists I have known belonged to the most diverse professions: lawyers, physicians, theologians, philologists, business men, politicians, writers, actors, workmen, gardeners, artisans, etc. However, certain professions furnish a greater number of Uranists than others, although we cannot give exact figures. The following are to be especially noted: actors, writers, florists, furniture dealers, decorators, cooks, hair-dressers, dressmakers. It seems that many Uranists are attracted by these professions which cater rather to women, because of their aptitude for decorating apartments, the making of women's apparel, etc. Moreover, it is easily understood why Uranists become dressmakers: they are quite successful because of their falsetto voices and the grace with which they perform feminine movements.

Hartmann has observed that among spiritualists and mediums in particular, are a great many sexual inverts. Even though a certain profession attracts Uranists, one must not expect to find sexual inverts among the greater number of members of this profession. If we admit, for example, that among 100 Uranists there are found ten dressmakers, one must not forget on the other hand, that among 500 inhabitants there is on the average one dressmaker. In this way the relative number of Uranist dressmakers will not be exaggerated.

So far as Uranism among soldiers is concerned, I have it from the lips of a Uranist that his companions are rarely attracted by the army, and that when they make a name therein for themselves, it is more likely in the theoretical phase of the profession. This opinion, however, is not general. It suffices to mention, among the great leaders, Julius Caesar, Charles XII, Tilly. However, as regards Tilly, I have found nothing that could confirm this accusation directed by Uranists themselves. It is true that Tilly avoided all relations with women; but it would be false to consider this peculiarity as a proof of his Uranistic habits. Prince Eugene is likewise accused of practicing love in the manner of the ancient **Greeks.**

It would be equally interesting to know exactly in what proportion the Jews figure among the Uranists. I know several who practice homosexual love. However, according to a communication of a person well versed in the matter the number of Uranist Jews may be small in view of their proportion in the total population. This is not in accord with the statistics of Gock and of N. N. I believe that Uranists are found among the Jews in the same proportion as they are among the other races.

As to the ages of the Uranists, I would say that the youngest I have had occasion to observe was sixteen years old and the oldest sixty-eight. However Uranists I have known have told me that their perversions appeared towards the age of ten or twelve or even sooner. I know one in whom sexual perversion appeared when he was three years old. At **this age he exhibited an extraordinary desire for men. There is** therefore no doubt that one ought actually to find a great many Uranists among youngsters, even before their sixteenth birthday. It must be added that in sexual inverts the genital instinct awakes appreciably earlier than in normal individuals. But I cannot say whether sexual perversion subsides sooner than the normal genital instinct. For example, the old **man** of sixty-eight of whom I have just spoken, today has sexual intercourse with a man about once a week. I know of certain individuals who at an advanced age continue to satisfy their perverse instincts. An old man of eighty-two, who died recently conserved until the last his habits of sexual inversion; in the Uranist world, he was known by the feminine nickname of "Grandmother."

Although sexual perversion manifests itself among men by psychic and abnormal sexual tendencies, the individual is generally perfectly normal physically and anatomically. The bodies of such individuals have been examined with a view to finding any modifications caused by sexual perversions. There may have been found certain anomalies in the conformation of the penis. In certain Uranists the virile member attains to dimensions no greater than those of a little boy. In other cases the penis has been found to be abnormally long. A Uranist observed by Krafft-Ebing affirmed that in the state of erection of his penis measured ten inches and five inches in circumference. But in most cases there is not to be found any anomaly in this respect. Neither do the testicles present any appreciable modifications. In a case observed by Westphal, the testicles were of ordinary dimensions and could be easily pushed back into the anal canal; but even this case, there could be no question of establishing a relation between this anomaly and the sexual perversion of the patient.

The erections of the Uranists are in general normal and vigorous, and the virile member, while in the state of erection, presents the same physical aspect (direction, etc.) as those in normal individuals. It is easily understood that in those who have abused themselves through masturbating, the erection can be lacking at times same as in those men who have had normal coition with women too frequently. A physician who has communicated with Krafft-Ebing on the subject of his own malady, and who has given him a detailed account of its history, affirms that he had had intercourse with more than 600 Uranists, without ever finding among them any malformation of the genital organs. The pubic hair is well developed in the Uranists. Some of them have little hair on their bodies, while possessing a full beard. Others have a very light beard. I know one who approached his thirtieth birthday and had hardly any hair on his chin.

It is also said that the Uranists present a considerable development of the mammilary glands. In one of his observations, Krafft-Ebing reports the history of a Uranist who affirms that he had in his breasts, from the age of thirteen to fifteen, milk which one of his friends drank. Among certain Uranists I have found at the elevations of the mamillary regions, an accumulation of adipose tissue rounding the breasts like those of a woman; but I have never observed very characteristic development of these glands. Some Uranists may be noted by their very small feet.

Uranists often distinguish themselves by their passion for music and the other arts. Coffignon has already cited this love for music as one of the peculiarities of the Uranist character. Artistic natures are very numerous among Uranists. They often possess a remarkable talent for acting. There is no satisfactory explanation for this. I believe that this talent must be attributed in large measure to the habit of lying which clings to the Uranist during his entire life. I also believe that their ability to place themselves in another situation and enter completely into another role also depends on a certain disposition of the central nervous system as does sexual perversion itself. At times very remarkable poets may be met with among Uranists. They excel above all in love poems addressed to men. The longing they feel is like that which urges the lover to sing of the perfections of his beloved. The religious sentiments of the Uranists manifests itself later in life when, after a life of sin, they seek to shelter themselves from their past.

In certain cases, during the time when sexual perversion shows itself, there is to be observed a complete change in the mode of life, carriage, character, costume, which then assume an entirely feminine aspect. This phenomenon is known as effeminization. Ramsdohr has observed that certain persons who, according to external signs belong to the feminine sex have a more masculine nature than some ordinary men. The case of Count Cajus, observed and described by Casper, is here interesting: Casper was struck by the entirely feminine mode of life of the Count who was accused of pederasty. Tardieu likewise insists on the effeminate character of pederasts. The desire to feel entirely feminine goes so far with thse individuals that a patient observed by Hammond often wished to cut off his genitals.

If the data of physiology and of psychology were examined, one would find feminine tendencies having sexual perversion as a basis. Langet is right in saying that as new

organs and new functions develop, new ideas appear. It is
therefore easy to comprehend why one sees in Uranists the
appearance with love for men, new ideas, ideas of coquetry,
of refinement of costume, etc.—ideas found in all women
who experience normal urge towards men. The tendency
towards effeminization sometimes appears in infancy. The
following is an example which shows it clearly: X., twenty-
eight years of age, has never experienced any urge for women.
While quite young, he loved to play with dolls, take walks
dressed as a girl, and devote himself to feminine occupations.
Even today, instead of devoting himself to his business, he
prefers to cook, sew, etc.; he willingly walks out dressed as
a woman. X. does not wear a beard, and holds one in such
horror that he hires a special barber to shave him closely.
When he wishes he speaks with a falsetto voice. He did so
once in my presence and I found he had vocal organs th~'
were quite feminine. He very often plays in comedies, a~
chooses feminine roles in which he is quite successful.

Ulrichs insists that the relations, environment and socia'
position oblige Uranists artificially to assume masculine mannerisms. "We play the man in life," he says, "just as we
play the woman in the theatre." As children Uranists regard
with anger the prohibition placed upon girls' games and
from pursuing feminine occupations.

It is indeed surprising to determine the power with which the
feminine temperament manifests itself among the Uranists.
When one thinks that the education they receive is in every
respect the same as that of normal boys, it is quite astonishing to see with what force feminine tendencies appear in their
character. And it is much more surprising that, in the first
place, Uranists have little love for effeminate men and are
rather attracted to vigorous normal men; and that, in the
second place, due to their effeminate manners they cause
themselves to be taken for women by normal men. Despite
everything they habituate themselves to their effeminization
as though they were urged by an invincible force.

The effeminate manners of the Uranists appears above all

when they are dressed as women. The masculine costume gives, even to the feminine type, a typically virile aspect, which by an involuntary association, produces the idea of a man. But if by chance one meets Uranists dressed as women or sees their photographs one is easily fooled and really believes that he is confronted by women. I know a case of this kind in which a very sagacious judge thus imagined himself for quite a while to be having an affair with a woman.

An observation, published by Taylor in the "Medical Jurisprudence" and reproduced by Tarnowsky, shows to what point Uranists can go in their tendency to appropriate the manners of women and of wearing their clothing. It had to do with a celebrated English actress, Elise Edwards, who appeared on several European stages and who was not recognized as a man until after his death. From his early youth this person had assumed feminine mannerisms and loved to dress as a woman. His genitals were held against his body by a special apparatus. This is practiced among Uranists today, if I am to believe an individual who frequents their meeting places.

Froenkel published the history of a man whom he called "homo mollis." This individual experienced the desire to dress as a woman whenever he could. He very carefully devoted his attention to his breasts and hips. What was at first only in the nature of play, later became a veritable passion. His walk, his voice, everything in him, took on a feminine character; he finally gave himself a girl's name. Besides, it has been pointed out that this man was a passive pederast. Westphal, from whom I borrow this fact, attributed some of the phenomena to the weakness of will of the individual in question, and to uphold this hypothesis, he cites the patient's fantasy of giving himself a girl's name. I believe, however, that the actual case ought to be interpreted in just the opposite way. The man had probably begun with feminine tastes, which manifested themselves in feminine occupations and his desire to dress like a woman. This inclination became violent enough to force the patient little by little to identify himself completely as a woman, which would have overtaken him even without his possessing a weak will.

The sexual urge of the same individual was abnormal, and its anomaly was closely connected with his mode of living. Besides, Westphal himself believes that Froenkel has confused cause with effect in supposing that the feminine type was developed in the patient through his female occupations.

And now let me cite a case which I have observed personally in Berlin. It concerns a Uranist who feels that he has a nature entirely feminine, and has sexual intercourse only with men and he prefers to dress like a woman. I carefully observed him one day, assisted by a police-agent in a secluded place. He was dressed like a woman. I was quite astonished to meet him in Friedrichstrasse several days later in the same costume. The police are greatly concerned with forbidding disguises of this kind. In fact, it happens rather often that thieves succeed more easily in putting the police on a wrong track by assuming the feminine garb. Likewise, men cause a scandal by their disguise, sometimes incurring severe punishment, which nevertheless (and it is well to recognize the fact), does not succeed in repressing this passion for parading in the garments of the other sex.

The Uranist of whom I have just spoken feels at his ease only in female attire; and even more, he is obliged to dress like a woman to be able to satisfy his sexual needs. Like a great many other Uranists he does not feel any desire for Uranists themselves. What attracts him more than anything else is an ordinary man (that is to say, a sexually normal man), vigorous, with a full beard. The sexual act which he must accomplish is the following: To take the other's member *in os* and at the same time to place his member on some part of the other's body. As he rarely finds men who consent to this kind of copulation, he has recourse to a subterfuge. He seeks to attract the attention of the men who please him: these, in turn, seeing him dressed like a woman believe that they are having an affair with one. When an acquaintance has been struck, the overtures made, the Uranist persuades the other that common coition does not afford so much pleasure as *membrum in os*. Then he conceals his own member by holding it between his thighs, while the erection is not complete, and by taking as much precaution as possible, he hides it with his shirt or with his hands. Two false rubber breasts succeed in fooling his partner.

Many Uranists, no doubt, proceed in the same way, when it is a matter of satisfying their passion. I have it from an absolutely reliable source that a Uranist of Berlin has served for quite a while as chambermaid in a hotel finding this means very useful in playing his feminine role to its desired conclusion.

We have just seen that a great many Uranists find their pleasure in carrying a complete wardrobe of women. But even when it is otherwise certain peculiarities of their costumes are sufficient witness to their feminine tendencies. They like to wear curls, or dress their hair as women do. Others comb their eyebrows, ornament themselves with jewelry and with bracelets; they often wear ear rings especially when they are in the company of other Uranists.

Many like to be seen in decolleté; others, like women, hold handkerchiefs in their hands. The fan plays a great role with them; they have, in holding it, a grace all their own. Certain articles of their dress are directly borrowed from the wardrobe of women. I know some who wear only very long stockings, and who feel quite ill at ease when they wear socks. Others wear shoes that not only have high heels but that are also just like women's shoes in every respect.

Uranists also like to wear corsets and they tighten them so that they may appear as slim as possible. I know one who always has a tape-measure with him in order to show off to the others the small measurements of his waist-line. It measures no more than 21.5 inches. Some Uranists have their corsets tightened that they fall in a faint while dancing. To insure a very tight lacing some hang suspended by the hands during the process.

When Uranists appear in society, at a ball for example, they willingly powder themselves and make up their faces much as women do. It is unebelievable to what extent they can go in this art; their ability to doll themselves is unimaginable. Naturally, and in this they are just like women, Uranists deny having recourse to any artifices. A Uranist who has furnished me with a great deal of valuable information about the mode of life of his companions has affirmed that nothing would anger the Uranists more than my exposing their artifices of make up. As this individual puts it: "Accuse them of having mean characters, of being thieves, of being capable of the worst crime; you would shock them less than by publicly denouncing their coquetry."

Let us here recall a passage in Xenophon's "Banquet" in which mention is made of men who love to anoint themselves with perfumed oils; let us add, however, that Socrates considered this habit unworthy of men. Many Uranists use perfumed writing paper. When they wish to, Uranists succeed in hiding their effeminate habits sufficiently to mislead a stranger. They reveal their true natures only on taking their leave. On the other hand, others show off their effeminacy.

A great many Uranists whose type recalls very much that of women, have their beard and mustache closely shaved, not so much as to arouse the passions of other Uranists, as to appear externally as much as possible like women. In fact, we shall see, further on, that Uranists are attracted much less to individuals of their own kind than towards mean of a clearly masculine type. A great many of them do not hesitate in taking depilatory measures to rid themselves of their beards, and in employing all the artifices of the toilette to make themselves appear as much as possible like women.

The apartments of the Uranists, and their furnishings very much resemble those of women. A person well acquainted with their habits has told me that their beds are furnished with canopies and their dressing tables are replete with articles used by women. They often ornament their apartments with pictures and statues representing good-looking youths.

Casper has already commented on it. It appears they love the statue of Apollo Belvedere in a manner all their own.

While most men do not like dancing, the Uranists have a veritable passion for that form of exercise. They dance with quite a feminine grace and prefer as Krafft-Ebing has already observed to dance rather with men than with women. This fact may be observed particularly at balls, where men dance with each other.

One of the peculiarities of Uranists is their ability to sew. Some know how to knit, others to crochet. And what is curious, is the fact that it is not the aptness of which they show ability in this kind of occupation but the inclination which urges them to it. If they refrain entirely from it it is because they fear betraying themselves. Gifts, resulting from their own labor, play a great role in the Uranists' world. I have personally seen gifts offered by one Uranist to another as a love token.

The handwriting of Uranists sometimes is like that of women and I have been able to establish the fact in two cases. However, I confess that my knowledge of graphology is not so comprehensive as to enable me to express myself in the matter with authority. It is also said that sexual perverts do not smoke much; but I know, on the other hand, the Uranists purposely become heavy smokers in order to avoid betrayal. They are likewise said to abstain from strong liquor.

The voice and language of Uranists play a very great role. It is a fact that in the normal state the female voice posesses a quality and a range different from those of the male voice; when the male imitates the female voice, the result is known as a falsetto. Now, this type of voice is sometimes quite pronounced in Uranists. In the case of two of them I would have certainly believed in hearing them speak that I was in the presence of women, had I not known in advance that they were men. When speaking Uranists assume this voice. They do so with ease; and even when in a gathering of normal individuals they find it difficult to speak in a normal tone, so easily and naturally does the falsetto voice come to them.

But while in certain Uranists the voice spontaneously assumes feminine characteristics, others expend much energy in acquiring them. It is not easily seen why. It is certainly not to attract other Uranists since, as we have said, Uranists do not seek to find falsetto voices in normal and vigorous men towards whom they feel themselves attracted. What appears to me more likely is that it is due to the existence of a sort of instinctive impulse which urges them to effeminacy, insofar as the voice is concerned, as well as the other peculiarities of the feminine character.

Among the signs of effeminacy to be found in Uranists, there are some which show quite clearly the connection between the phenomenon in question and the sexual instinct. It could have been believed that the latter had nothing to do directly with the voice. But, when we find Uranists' voices changed or only on the way to being modified, we ought to ask ourselves what connection there is between the falsetto voice and the sexual perversion. I do not know whether, at the same time, appreciable modifications take place in the larynx: at any rate, it would be a very interesting study to make. The male vocal cords are known to be a third longer than those of females or of children. Now Owen and Darwin insist on the fact that castration arrests the growth of the thyroid cartilage, which accompanies the lengthening of the vocal cords. The influence of the sexual life on the larynx further manifests itself in children, in modifications in the voice which, at the time of puberty, takes on many characteristics. Darwin makes this modification depend on the immoderate use that living being make of their voices at the time of love making and on the transmission through heredity of the artificial connections between the voice and the sexual life.

Moral contagion may here also play a certain part in the sense that the Uranist is led to assume a falsetto voice by frequently being in the society of his fellow Uranists.

I need not mention the fact that man's voice acquires the virility as he approaches the period of puberty, that before this period his voice resembles that of a little girl. In some Uranists, the voice seems to have normal masculine characteristics, only the deep quality is late in appearing—towards the age of eighteen and sometimes even later. Among other things the voice becomes peculiarly affected or pathetic. It is above all when they are under the influence of alcoholic liquor that Uranists make unmistakable use of the falsetto voice. In their intimate reunions, while having coffee, they speak in that voice. Sometimes their voice does not differ at all from that of a normal man except that it is extraordinarily slow and deep.

We have it on the authority of Ulrichs that Uranists like women do not know how to whistle and that they have much difficulty in learning to do so. I have been able neither to establish or confirm this fact. In this connection I have questioned a great many Uranists, and I have become convinced that they know how to whistle as well as normal men.

The walk of Uranists is often typical: they balance themselves on their haunches and walk affectedly, very much as women do. While walking they take little steps and raise their knees rather high by which characteristic they may be pointed out even in a crowd.

They also effect a position of the arms which is frequently seen in women. This position is difficult to describe. It consists in applying the forward part of the back of the hand to the cheek and in advancing the forearm from the body, while at the same time, lightly holding the elbow.

If one were to consider Uranism as a manifestation and proof of a debased character, it would be entirely useless to study the relation between character and the sexual tendencies of the Uranists. And even while admitting as possible the existence of a homo-sexual tendency, its satisfaction ought not be considered as the manifestation of a debased character. The Uranist seeks the satisfaction of his desire with the same passion as the man who is desirous of coition with a woman.

It is an intimate function independent of will and ethnic motives, and has nothing to do with good or evil. To judge the Uranist, we psychologists and naturalists ought to rid ourselves of the contempt with which we regard him.

But though we do not wish to commit ourselves entirely on the morality of the Uranist, we cannot hide the fact that his character presents certain phases that have little to recommend them and are even subjects for contempt. Envy, cowardice, which Gyurkovechky considers as peculiarities in the character of the impotent in general, are not to be found always in sexual perverts inflicted with impotence. It may be even asked whether these facts, brought to light by Gyurkovechky, really exist in individuals inflicted with genital impotence. It is certain however, as we have already said several times, that the character of the Uranist resembles that of a woman much more than that of a man.

Among the characteristic peculiarities of the Uranist, must be mentioned indiscretion, loquaciousness, caprice, and the tendency to lie. If it is difficult to study the character of the Uranists because they lie on all occasions. Furthermore, I have attributed to my observations the authentic character of a fact, only when I was absolutely certain of the source of my information or when I was able to make the observation myself. N. N. writes me as follows: "Believe me, the most hysterical and the most deceitful women are to be found among us Uranists; for women we are, and we do not deny it." How are we to explain this tendency to dissimulate? It may be by the fact that Uranists are obliged to involve themselves all their lives in a tissue of lies, for it is rare that they would confide their secret to a strange person. Even when they are among themselves they are not sincere in speaking of their sexual lives. They do not hesitate to confess being attracted spiritually by this or that person, but they vigorously deny having sexual intercourse with him. It must be believed that this daily lying habituates them always to lie. But that would not explain all. I rather believe that the reason for this dissimulation must be sought in the truly hysteri-

cal and feminine tendencies of the Uranists. Among Uranists
are to be found, rather frequently, certain characteristic traits
which are also found in certain hysterical women; on the
other hand, hysterical signs, such as pains in the abdomen,
involuntary muscular contractions, headaches, hysteric fits,
etc., are not more frequent among Uranists than among
normal men. I desire to raise this point for, ordinarily, hysteria is considered as a pecular privilege of the feminine sex.
Cansbatt considers hysterical men as soft and effeminate.

But just as all women are not given to lying, and as a
great many hysterical people are passionately in love with
the truth, we also find that there are Uranists who tell the
truth. I know some who while confiding to no one the secrets of their sexual lives are absolutely trustworthy, and
let me add that their communications have been of the greatest use to me. The lie is encountered principally among
Uranists who belong to the underworld; their communications moreover even when they appear to be made with the
greatest sincerity ought to be carefully verified.

Coffignon draws our attention to a certain affected polite-
ness which may be a sign common to all Uranists. It really
exists. What also characterize the Uranists are certain in-
sipidly soft manners, most often hiding a subtle hypocrisy.
The vanity of the Uranists is often unbelieveable. At balls
and parties one tries to eclipse the other. I know one who
after each party asks of all whether he was not "the most
beautiful" in his costumes. He possesses a great variety
of costumes; he appears dressed sometimes as a flapper,
sometimes as a ballet dancer, etc.

The Uranist calls to our mind the vain woman, and we
find in him all the characteristics of such a woman. His envy
and his jealousy do not stop at little things (and such also
is the vain woman) and he may experience for example, a
feeling of satisfaction in having a slimmer figure than others.
The Uranist passes hours before his mirror admiring himself
in his costumes, to see whether he is well dressed, etc.
Schultze rightfully says, in his book "Folly of Modes," that

religious respect for fashion is a characteristic trait of women; that is why we consider effeminate those nincompoops and fops who follow all the caprices of style. The same author remarks, very justly, that "chic" people follow professions that are quite accessible to men as well as to women. This fact agrees with what we have said of the preference of Uranists for certain professions.

We cannot over-estimate the passion of the Uranists for Jewelry. The vanity of the Uranists shows itself in other ways. They are rather frequently given to boasting of their amorous adventures.

All of this constitutes a very unfavorable picture of the Uranist character; it should not be concluded from this that the characteristic traits we have just described are to be found in all Uranists. On the contrary, I wish to say that there are men inclined with sexual perversion whose characters are faultless.

Modesty is one of the characteristics which distinguish women from men. It is interesting to note that according to certain authors modesty is much more developed in the Uranist than in the normal man. There are Uranists who avow that during their childhood and even during puberty they were to be distinguished from their comrades by their modesty. According to Tarnowsky, the modesty of Uranists even while they are children manifests itself in an abnormal fashion. It is thus that this sentiment would show itself especially before a strange man: children, with a predisposition to Uranism are less inclined to undress themselves before a man than before a woman.

One should not conclude that all Uranists possess feminine characteristics. On the contrary. there are "real" Uranists whom aside from their sexual perversion act in everything else as men: they do not like to dress themselves as women, have manly tastes, go horseback riding, are much given to gymnastics, athletics, etc.

From these latter must be distinguished those who, through habit and necessity, play the role of the normal man when in society. But as soon as they are once in the intimate circle of their companions their feminine natures immediately reappear especially when they are under the influence of liquor.

One of Krafft-Ebing's patients maintains that only 10 per cent of the Uranists prefer feminine occupations. However, this assertion ought not to be taken literally, inasmuch as the same patient also maintains that most Uranists are active pederasts. Now, my personal studies, in accord with those of modern authors show rather that Uranists are most often passive pederasts.

One must carefully guard against considering all effeminate traits as a sure proof of Uranistic tendencies. There are men presenting such and such a feminine trait who are nevertheless absolutely normal sexually.

There exists a whole category of men who during their childhood conduct themselves as little girls, love dolls, and do not like to play soldiers, or war; they later become normal from every point of view. Again, the observation may be made of boys who principally toward the period of puberty are seized with a veritable love for their comrades; later this sentiment is directed only toward women, and it is then impossible to find in them any traces of homosexual tendencies.

We must now study the influence of sexual perversion on the relations between the Uranist and the moral man. Let us first see what the Uranist himself thinks of his condition.

Certain Uranists try for a while to fool themselves about the truth of their condition by attributing the sexual attraction which men exercise over them to a sentiment of friendship. They seek to find in the man those qualities capable of explaining the urge they experience and they forget that they are only deluding themselves. Unlike Westphal, Krafft-Ebing thinks that sexual perversion does not make the Uranist unhappy and that they are unhappy only insofar as the conventions of society and the law oppose them in satisfying their passions. I am in entire accord with this opinion and I believe that the unhappiness of the Uranist is the result of this repression. It is equally true that in many cases, as

Krafft-Ebing found them, sexual perversion does not render perverts unhappy.

A Uranist who is conscious of his condition does not regard it as normal, although he is far from considering himself ill. It appears to me very interesting to report a conversation between two Uranists, N. N. of a cool and tranquil nature, and M. X. "If only," said N. N., "sexual perversion were considered not as a crime, but as a pathologic condition." "That is not my opinion," replied M. X., "and I even prefer the present state of things. Today we are provided with a lawyer, while were sexual perversion considered a malady, we would be packed into a mad house."

Certain Uranists, like Ulrichs for example, recognize the insufficiency of their love as compared to normal love. A great many of them really suffer under the idea that they cannot have a family of their own because of the unfortunate desire, and they consider their lives as incomplete. I have known some who were certainly more capable of playing the role of head of a family than many a normal man.

Certain Uranists who are married, experience a real annoyance by being compelled, in order to satisfy their passion, to have sexual intercourse with men. They consider themselves unfaithful to their wives. Some make themselves miserable by the idea that they are the only ones inflicted with this abnormal passion. Such are found in the upper classes of society and in small cities where Uranists acquaint themselves less easily with each other. They therefore lead quite an unhappy existence; for they are quite conscious of their condition, without knowing that there are thousands like them. The consciousness of their lacking the power to master this passion further magnifies their misery. There are also a great many of them who are in a state of very acute depression.

In those Uranists who consider their condition as unfortunate and who continually reproach themselves for it are also found other psychic and physical ailments; hypochondria, melancholia, dyspepsia, etc. These troubles are also found when the Uranist is smitten with an unfortunate love. On the contrary, the Uranist who is happy in his love for a man becomes immediately gay and well disposed.

Although the Uranist often and very sincerely complains of his lot his unfortunate passion rarely leads to suicide. Personally I do not know of a case of suicide nor of an attempt of that nature among the Uranists. But an unrequited love for a man, the fear of blackmail or of figuring in a law suit may indirectly force a Uranist to suicide. I have it from a reliable source that a well-known man of letters killed himself several years ago to avoid the shame of a law suit in which there would have been revealed his abnormal passion. Suicide as a result of sexual perversion was discussed at the Medico-Psychological Society of Berlin on the occasion of an observation of Hutchinson's reported by Hirschberg.

Tarnowsky sees things a little too much on the dark side. The spirit of Tarnowsky's book does not correspond with the observations I have had occasion to make. It seems that the material used in this book was collected in a private Uranist circle; that in Russia, and more especially in St. Petersburg, the customs of the Uranists are not the same as they are in Germany. In Germany one does not so frequently meet with pederasty in sexual perversion. I cannot agree with Tarnowsky in his confusion between sexual perversion and the underworld where men sell themselves, for in Berlin homosexuality and masculine prostitution are quite different.

To satisfy their sexual instinct Uranists are obliged to have sexual intercourse with men. There are some among them who are disgusted by the act and regret it; they consider it immoral. Nevertheless, these feelings do not protect them against a new satisfaction of their passion, even as the fear of remorse does not prevent a normal man from having coition with a woman. Here we find ourselves face to face with a well-known phenomenon which Hartmann tried to define when he said that the non-satisfaction of an impulse is worse for an individual than its excessive satisfaction.

Scholz has published a case that is interesting because he records the actual expressions of the patient, showing quite

well with what disgust he regarded the sexual act toward
which he was irresistibly drawn. I have often drawn the
same conclusion from the remarks of a great many Uranists
who could do nothing against their passion.

Now let us see how Uranists act toward women. There
are some who during a very long period are not conscious of
their true condition; they try to have sexual intercourse with
women and are quite surprised to find that they remain impotent before them. Others are quite clearly disgusted with
women, and do not seek to have sexual intercourse with
them, and they are surprised to see other males so powerfully
attracted towards the feminine sex. They have not reached
that stage where they are conscious that their sexual sensations are quite different from those of normal men. I know
cases in which individuals have become conscious of their
condition only on approaching their twentieth year when they
have become passionately enamored of other men.

I know a man who, to the age of twenty-two, was quite
normal, insofar as he had relations with women without
experiencing any passion for men. One day he met a
man whose image, ever after, followed him day and night:
he had erections in thinking of him, and ejaculated one day
when he succeeded in embracing him. From that moment
the unfortunate man understood his condition. I believe that
it is much more often in this way than through the realization of impotence towards women that Uranists become
aware of their sexual perversion.

The discovery of their perversion, of their aversion to
women, has quite a variable reaction on the Uranist's spirit;
some accept their new condition in rather a matter-of-fact
way, and there is not to be found in them that feeling of pre-
mature old age that an author ascribes to early impotence.
The degree of aversion that the Uranist feels for women may
vary, going from mere antipathy to the greatest horror. For
some of them the idea of a nude woman is repulsive even
without the idea of contact. I know some Uranists who have
attempted coition with a woman and whom the disgust caused

by the contact forced to leave the room. There are others who have relations with women (relations quite platonic, be it understood), although sexually they have intercourse only with men.

Certain Uranists affect pleasure in the society of women, and I know some whom in Berlin, have the reputation of men of affairs. Indeed, Uranists prefer to acquire this reputation rather than have their passion suspected. They easily succeed in misleading their friends—those who form their society—by their purely psychic and intellectual relations with women. I have been told the history of a young man of Berlin who each day was seen in the company of different women of more than doubtful morality and who nevertheless could say with Tilly that he never touched a woman in his life.

There are other Uranists who carefully avoid the society of women and pass as model young men. Indeed, it is not difficult for them, with their desire for men to conserve their chastity in their relations with women. It is quite possible that more than one historic person noted for their chastity owe their reknown simply to their sexual perversion.

We know that there are a great many Uranists who are married. This fact may lead to error, when it concerns historic personages and hide their Uranistic tendencies. Such, for example, was Frederick I, King of Wurtenberg, who reigned from 1797 to 1816. He was married twice and had several children, one of whom succeeded him; one of his daughters married Jerome, King of Westphalia. Nevertheless, there is every reason to believe that Frederick I was a pederast. Infamous men, like the notorious Count von Dillon, exploited the passion of the king for handsome youths in order to dominate him. This count had poor young nobles come from Mecklenburg to absorb all of the country's revenues that the upkeep of the court could leave over.

Some of them are psychic hermaphrodites who have sexual intercourse at times with their wives, at times with a man; others have sexual intercourse only with men. I know a Berlin household, the husband thereof being a declared Uranist; the wife takes her revenge by entertaining men, without going too much out of her way. However, these households are not always unhappy, for a moral and very straight bond is often established between the Uranist husband and his wife. At times, Uranists prove even to be fertile. To have coition with his wife, the Uranist takes advantage of accidental erections, or he induces them by picturing a man to himself while he ejaculates in the vagina.

Although coition may be thus made possible Uranists do not practice it much because of the fatigue it causes them. When, in imagining a naked man they have an erection the ejaculation which follows causes them great fatigue and gives them no satisfaction at all. A Uranist whose history has been published by Scholz, was married to a beautiful woman. He had sexual intercourse with her only twice, despite their long life in common. He said that physical contact with his wife disgusted him; this is also said by certain patients of Krafft-Ebing's.

Following is what a Uranist writes me in regards to his sexual relations: "I can resume my sexual relations with women in which I have always played a passive role. Curiosity, self-love, vanity, ignorance of my desires, have forced me from time to time to attempt coition with women. I have always hoped to cure myself of my unhealthy tendencies by practicing the acts of normal love. Under the exciting influence of alcoholic liquors I can accomplish the sexual act very well although at the supreme moment the sexual pleasure is always lacking. The beauty of the woman leaves me cold. However, I have not before me the image of a man during the coitus. I induce an erection by energetically rubbing against the woman and by mechanical movements, and ejaculation soon follows. Several times my attempts have not succeeded. For six years I have not had sexual intercourse with women; whatever little satisfaction I derive from it is of no use." Tarnowsky notes that an individual, who in a normal condition is opposed to the accomplishment of an unnatural sexual act, easily consents to do so while in a state of intoxication when he is no longer in possession of himself and when his sensual curiosity is excited. I know several cases analogous to the one I report in which individuals incapable of accomplishing a normal sexual act in an ordinary condition become perfectly capable of doing so while under the influence of alcohol.

The above letter proves that sexual perversion ought not all to be confounded with the impossibility of practicing coition. Uranists can even have a great many children since their sperms are entirely normal.

Certain Uranists are viewed with much favor by women who are quite proper and they pass even as "lions." If they succeed so well with women it is certainly because of their morbid predisposition. Due to this they are better acquainted than ordinary men with the conversation of women and know better how to reply. Sometimes they owe their success to spending much time, as some of them have confessed to me, with neglected ladies and with old maids.

The Uranist finds himself often attracted to women, without this attraction's having anything to do with the sexual urge. He can very well appreciate beauty in women. He finds pleasure in talking to intelligent women. In all this, the sensual side is completely missing. It is as disagreeable for a Uranist to embrace a pretty woman as for a normal man to embrace another man, as handsome as he may be. It also often happens that a woman becomes enamored of a Uranist putting the latter into a very difficult position knowing how impossible it is for him to reciprocate her love. There are women with keen insight who divine the true tendencies of the Uranist without however being exactly conscious of it. Thus a very cultured and very intelligent woman said to N. N., that she judged him incapable of experiencing love for women.

I now come to a very interesting point: namely, the relations between Uranists and the way in which they make each other's acquaintance. They usually say that they recognize each other at first sight on the street and elsewhere. This assertion is to be found in almost all the books dealing with sexual perversion and it is to be noted in various autobiographies of Uranists. As N. N. tells me, this faculty of recognizing each other at first sight is a sort of dogma among the Uranists. N. N. himself considers this assertion as absolutely false. It is one of the legends which is current among the Uranists and in which they very sincerely believe. A great many of them recognize each other by a sort of eye language. Uranists no doubt often come to an understanding by thus regarding each other in the street.

When a man follows a woman who pleases him, he tries to attract her attention; in the same way, if Uranist A encounters man B who pleases him, he turns, looks at him, and forces his attention. If B is also a Uranist he understands A's manoeuvers and responds in like manner. ·There is nothing in all this that is mysterious or supernatural. A Uranist told me that they easily understand each other insofar as their desires and tendencies were concerned through movements and other signs. Uranists and individuals of the underworld especially make themselves known to each other in the street by the further expedients of asking the time, a glass of beer, a match for their cigarette, etc. In Berlin the Uranists prefer to meet in public places.

Sometimes while intoxicated they expose themselves by assuming their falsetto voices or by addressing each other by their feminine nicknames. They frequently change their rendezvous. But ordinarily, their conduct in the cafes leaves nothing to be desired. Those who are not acquainted with the ways of the Uranists cannot distinguish them from the habitual clients; but once initiated; they easily pick them out by their manners, their way of speaking and the glances which they cast from table to table.

Uranists often form small circles of three to twelve persons among whom may be observed a spirit of friendship. But this custom is not general for a great many of them have no sympathy for each other even outside of sexual intercourse. In their parties they often very seriously celebrate official "engagements."

The Uranists also like to have intimate parties where they

can do so unmolested; sometimes they even hold balls. But above all, they prefer "Kaffe Klatches." In these parties the feminine character of the Uranists reveals itself most clearly. The facts which I am about to relate may appear unbelieveable; however, I have them from the lips of trustworthy Uranists. First of all, at these parties only coffee is drunk, and this purely feminine custom shows up somewhat the peculiar character of the Uranists. "Around the table men were seated wearing caps in the Hamburg fashion, some even in aprons. Each one had brought his work: one was knitting, another sewed, a third crocheted, and so on." Their conversation resembles that of men in no respect, and they speak neither of politics nor of science, etc. There's a veritable gossiping in which only stories of love, of jealousy, etc., play a part. In these parties Uranists allow themselves certain liberties; sometimes contacts are made without however passing the boundaries of what is permitted.

As we have said, Uranists also hold formal dances which are sometimes attended by as many as a hundred persons. There are few women present. Most of the men are dressed as women—as gypsies, Spanish dancers, Chinese, etc. The women present are ordinarily perverted: we shall speak of them again later. To the Uranists, the question as to what costume to wear is of much concern, for each desires to eclipse the others. Thus, after consulting as to which costumes to wear, a Uranist would say: "Just watch how my costume creates a sensation." At these balls the men dance with each other, their movements assuming quite a feminine grace. Uranists are quite enthusiastic about these dances because they are tired of always playing a part to avoid betrayal and there they are free to follow their own bents.

In Uranist society are to be found clearly different castes. A Uranist will never regard one of his companions as superior, but he will always regard with some contempt one of his colleagues who may hold an inferior position socially. A Jewish Uranist has told me that anti-semitism does not exist among his companions. I have been informed by another that he has often had intercourse with members of the nobility, without encountering among them what is known as aristocratic snobbishness. The same individual, however, considered as his inferiors those Uranists little favored by fortune—laborers, for example—and spoke of them with considerable contempt. Their passion causes social distinction to disappear completely for a time.

The nicknames used by Uranists make rather interesting study. In the first place their expressions are rather bizarre and picturesque. Thus they are often heard to use the word "wise." They say, for example, that V. is "wise" because he practices Uranism. If Y. is not "wise" it it because he is not a Uranist. To distinguish themselves from other classes of society, they speak of themselves as "true," that is to say, as being attracted exclusively to men. They also use the same epithet of "true" to differentiate themselves from the class of male prostitutes, the latter not being ordinarily sexual perverts. They designate a person who has the inclination for masculine love by saying that "he is still one of them."

Often the Uranists call each other "aunts" and "sisters." According to a patient of Krafft-Ebing's, the latter expression is the most frequently used among the Uranists of Vienna. Coffignon (in "Corruption in Paris") claims that the word "aunt" is likewise very much used in Paris, being applied generally to passive pederasts and more especially to those among them who professionalize in order to blackmail; sometimes they have intimate relations with prostitutes. In Berlin "aunt" becomes "aunt-ist" and instead of saying that so-and-so is a Uranist, one says that he is an "aunt-ist."

In order to distinguish the aunts among them, they are called Lisa, Martha, and so on. Further, to tell one Lisa from another (and there are many of them) each one has an extra nickname derived from peculiar characteristic traits or from some Uranist custom. Thus one Uranist is called Lisa the Handle because of his habit of placing his hands on his hips. The feminine names which the Uranists bear have no particular significance. It is to be noted that the Jewish

Uranists bear the names of Jewish women, such as Rebecca, Sarah, etc. Sometimes the Uranists give a feminine twist even to their family names. Occasionally the name is taken from the person with whom the Uranist has or has had sexual intercourse. A Uranist who had had relations with Baron X has long been known as "Madame the Baroness." Thus they speak of each other as Mrs. Muller or Mrs. Schultze to designate a Uranist whose name is Muller of Schultze.

The Uranists of Berlin and of other large cities know each other quite well. Even though they may not be acquainted with all their fellows they know by their conversation which are their new recruits.

In the presence of normal men Uranists are very reserved in regard to what concerns their lives in general and their sexual life in particular. It is very difficult to gain their confidence because of the contempt they generally encounter when they confess their morbid predisposition. This sufficiently explains the distrust evinced by Uranists, a distrust which for analogous reasons, is also displayed by deaf-mutes. And, like the deaf-mutes, the Uranist casts away his reserve and confides freely when he believes he has found a true friend.

When a Uranist visits a doctor to tell him of his life and to ask him to cure him of his malady he evidently does not cause the feeling of disgust that he provokes by his manners in the street or in other public places. I have witnessed Uranists shed bitter tears of despair while in my consultation room.

Tarnowsky is of the opinion that certain pederasts, the periodic pederasts in particular, seek the advice of doctors more than others. I have been able to confirm this opinion. According to Tarnowsky, the Uranists in large cities who become infected with a venereal disease (encountered among them from time to time) go to only one doctor and always the same one. I cannot say whether the same fact is true of Berlin. I have actually been told the name of one of these physicians but the source from whence this information comes does not appear to me to be very reliable.

Chapter IV

LOVE LIFE

Inverts, Passions; History of Doctor X; Erotomania; Jealousy, Passion, Murder; Inverts and Normal Men; Sex Inclinations; The Different Sex Acts. Active—Passive Pederasts; Fellatio, Masturbation; Imaginary Coition.

After having studied the life of the Uranists in general, I will now discuss their sexual life, their love affairs, and the manner in which they satisfy their sexual instinct.

The love of Uranists often assumes quite an ardent form. He thinks day and night of the man he loves, dogs his steps and floods him with avowals of his love and with demands for a rendezvous. Once I saw a Uranist enjoying the sight of a man he loved: the pleasure of seeing the person he loved showed on his face just as it does in a man who meets the woman he loves. Love renders the Uranist capable of the greatest sacrifices for the man he loves. In this respect the love of a Uranist may be compared to that of woman's love for man. Just as a woman's love is stronger and more unselfish than a man's so the Uranist's love may be superior in these respects to that of a normal man.

Sometimes the Uranist's love goes so far as to cause him to sacrifice his life. The unhappy man can resist neither the desires nor the claims of the beloved person and often becomes a mere instrument in the latter's hand just as in the

love between man and woman. This feeling of submission
is frequent among the Uranists and they find pleasure in it. Such
is the principle of masochism of which we shall speak again.

When the Uranist leaves the man he loves, the letters between them deal only of love. These letters are written in
the most passionate tones. Often, if not always, they seem
to be addressed to a woman and are signed with a woman's
name which is the name carried by the individual in the
Uranist world. I have seen a letter of Mr. X addressed to
his friend Y, which commences with "My sweet Anna" and
which is signed "Your Martha." I have also been shown a
photograph of a Uranist with the following inscription:

> Always correct, good-looking and smart;
> Thus women's blessings are obtained.

Tarnowsky has already drawn our attention to the passionate
character of the letters of Uranists.

Sometimes the love begun in youth is religiously guarded
by the Uranist during his entire life. I know some Uranists
separated for many years from the men they first loved who
were seized with an uncontrollable passion to see their first
loves. Others have affairs which last for years.

This passionate love sometimes manifests itself in early
youth. School boys, six or seven years old, sometimes experience profound sentiments of invert sexual nature. Certain of these youngsters confessed of having erections in their
relations with their comrades and of often satisfying themselves with obscene relations. A Uranist has declared to
Krafft-Ebing of having, at the age of ten, a profound feeling
for a good-looking boy, and of having all the ardent desires
which characterize love. Uranists confess of having often
had intimate relations with their schoolmates and of having
experienced peculiar exciting sensations when they were
seated beside a boy who pleased them.

The following history shows how far passion may cause
a Uranist to forget the fundamental rules of honesty and
even to commit a crime in spite of his honesty. A Berlin

Uranist A, of an upright character is in love with another Uranist B, with whom he has intimate relations. They often quarrel. At the termination of each dispute they forget their differences and become more devoted to each other. However A, who always fears to lose B's love conceived the criminal project of marrying his own sister to B. A loves his sister and is well aware of the sin he is about to commit. He knows that B could never perform his duties as husband, yet his passion for B is so violent that he is not even stopped by these considerations. A told me that B is a declared Uranist who has never shown the slightest regard for women. A desires to marry him to his sister so that he may meet B at all times without awakening suspicions.

I have in my possession a letter from a Uranist physician thirty-eight years old. It shows the impassioned character that love assumes among Uranists. At present he is involved in an unhappy love affair. The doctor in question fell in love with a man whom he suspects to be a Uranist. This man, being in love with a third, did not respond to the doctor's love. Here is what the doctor writes me in this connection in the autobiography he sent me: "In 1886, I met the man who changed my life to a great extent. He was young, amiable, and had an artistic temperament. He felt impassioned and tender friendship towards me, full of sacrifice and concern; but it was not love. I mistook these sentiments for a violent passion to which I responded with a love no less ardent. From this error came a series of conflicts so serious, so painful for me that I no longer found life worth living. My gaiety, my sleep, my work, all were lost because I could not have sexual intercourse with him. At first I made several attempts but they miscarried piteously. This everlasting disdain, the mortal wounding of my sentiments in my attempts to concentrate them on him alone almost killed me. He remained amiable and kind to me all the while. I sought an explanation of his conduct: why did he remain cold? This question tormented me all day and night. After a most painful conflict I wrote to him that I no longer wished to see him. He immediately came to me, cried like a baby and pleaded with me on his knees not to desert him. I weakened and I gave in to him. Everything was as before. Our relations were normal until the old desires reawakened; for the love that one bears for a person is deeply rooted in the being. No one could give me what I tried to get from him; new conflicts and new torments. Though I did not possess him I could not separate from him. He told me that he had no other friends and that he loved me above everything. I tried several times to avoid the course I was pursuing but all my attempts led to the same result. The impossibility of complete possession, my unsatisfied desire completely changed my spirit. The suspicions, the doubts that preyed upon my peace. The enigma which I faced each day, and for which I sought a solution, literally pounded my brain. [Indeed, the conduct of the other was very enigmatic; he acted towards the doctor as though he loved him, but absolutely refused sexual intercourse. It is likely that he experienced a purely psychic love for the unhappy doctor. Such strange behavior may be observed among Uranists who avoid having sexual intercourse with the man who does not excite them. Later, I shall return, among other things, to this psychic form of love.] This life continued for three years until I was prostrated both physically and morally. Then he in turn fell in love with a man. He told me about it one day; three weeks after it happened. At this declaration I felt that all the demons had been let loose in my breast and I thought of killing him and myself. The idea that all I desired for years would belong to another drove me insane. There was nothing left to me but to revolve in my morbid fancy his happiness and my misery. The love I felt changed into a desire for vengeance: I wished to kill the man he loved. I felt no jealousy properly so-called since no one deprived me of that which I possessed. My happiness was destroyed only by the person whom I loved."

Thus finished the description of the feelings experienced by the unhappy doctor. I knew him personally and I must say that I have never seen a patient so pitiable as this doctor. For a long time he was obsessed with the idea of avenging himself on the man he loved and who had refused to reciprocate this love. I heard from him again in a letter that was quite interesting. I cannot help quoting a passage:

"The acute consciousness of a betrayed passion deprived me of sleep so that I was obliged to use chloral. My dreams have been only the continuation of reality and just as painful. I do not yet know how all this will end; but the elemental impulses continue their course. I have already thought of quitting this world forever. I would have done so if I did not fear that my demon would depart with me. The only rational solution to this conflict is death but three others to whom I am intimately bound would be condemned to death by the same blow."

The doctor in question, who is the only provider for his family, has written to me again quite recently. He has succeeded by work to rid himself of these ideas of vengeance. These facts show to what violence the Uranist's passion may attain.

When the Uranist is happily in love his psychic and moral outlook become healthier, his faculty for work increases, just as in a normal man whose love is shared by the woman he loves. The moral and psychic conditions of the Uranist whose love is not shared, rapidly become the saddest imaginable; he ends by being obsessed with ideas of suicide which he sometimes commits. I knew a Uranist who would have committed suicide had he not been held back by the feeling of duty toward his family of which he was the sole support. It is probable that a great many unexplained suicides have no other cause than an unhappy Uranistic love. It is true that Uranists are capable of entertaining violent passions and to sacrifice themselves for the men they love yet I do not believe that their love can last a lifetime.

Sometimes the love of Uranists is purely psychic; that is to say, it does not end in the satisfaction of the sexual instincts: the sexual desires do not manifest themselves or they remain latent for a long time. These cases are rare but they certainly exist. I know a Uranist who cannot have sexual relations with other than normal men but who has love affairs with Uranists at the same time. These affairs are a kind of platonic love. It is hard to believe that such a love can last a long time. This platonic love is met with but seldomly among Uranists. In these cases the sexual act does not take place, not because of a sentiment of propriety or of fear of the law but simply because of the absence of any desire.

It is very difficult to say what is platonic love. It cannot be identified with friendship from which it is easily distinguished: for jealousy exists in one and is lacking in the other. Neither is it simple sexual love whose purpose is the satisfaction of the senses since the latter is excluded from platonic love. Neither can I admit that in platonic love is to be understood a love from which the sexual desires are excluded through social or moral motives; for if one were to admit this definition, platonic love would be nothing else but ordinary love in which the desires in question unmistakably exist but cannot be satisfied. Krafft-Ebing and a great many other authorities altogether deny the existence of platonic love. It may be asked, however, whether the conclusion is not made too quickly. According to communications I have received platonic love seems to exist among Uranists in whom it is characterized by a vague desire and without a conscious sexual urge. In these cases may be encountered another new form of platonic love in which there exists the desire to touch and to embrace the beloved person without the intervention of the genital senses. I believe that among the Uranists this form of love is least frequent. I personally cannot affirm the existence of platonic love, while I know definitely of the form characterized by the desire of touching the body with participation of the genital senses.

In certain cases the Uranist's love for a man goes so far that one may speak of it as erotamania, which is a psychic disturbance characterized by an excitation of all the senses having an erotic origin. According to Tarnowsky this fact may be observed especially in Uranists brought up among women and sheltered from the influence of pederasts. In erotomania in which the sexual desires disappear altogether love manifests itself principally in the form of an exalted admiration of the beloved person. Such admiration exists in cases which are not erotomania. Certain Uranists are excited, just as women are, by the essentially masculine qualities that they encounter in the man they love; virility, courage, firmness, etc.

In love between Uranists there is nevertheless to be found other peculiarities which characterize the normal love between man and woman. It is a notorious fact that there are artful women who, to cause themselves to be desired, affect a coldness towards the man to whom their sole desire is to give themselves. The same fact is to be observed among Uranists. A Uranist, A, made the acquaintance of another Uranist, B. But hardly had A perceived that B did not cease to look at him, then he immediately assumed an air of indifference, simply to make himself more ardently desired by B. And indeed, after some time, intimate relations were established between A and B, the latter being married, and these relations were upheld, as is often the case in this sort of relationship by numerous gifts on the part of one or the other. These gifts are most often in the form of jewelry; sometimes they are bits of embroidery or of tapestry; above all, when the Uranist, as is often the case, knows how to make them.

It should not be thought that love between Uranists does not give rise to quarrels. On the contrary, quarrels and disputes are frequent and provoked most often by jealousy. The existence of jealousy among Uranists is not at all astonishing, since we know that jealousy is the customary consequence of a passionate love. As not only the sexual urge but also the sentiment of love is often exaggerated in Uranists, it follows that the appearance of jealousy is quite natural. The following are examples taken from the Uranist world:

There exist in Uranist circles individuals known for the

most beautiful, a sort of "professional beauty," that all desire
to possess, just as in the normal world we speak of a very
pretty woman. Among these "professional beauties" figures
X, a singer who entertains intimate relations with another
Uranist, Y. The other Uranists try their best to stir up X
against Y; Z for example, who tries by all means to acquire
X's good-will and to awaken suspicion and jealousy in him,
does not hesitate to insinuate that Y entertains intimate relations with other men. And if in spite of all this Z does not
accomplish his end, he will not hesitate to employ a means
very much used among Uranists, which consists in menacing
X with a public accusation of his being a pederast.

Let me relate a case of jealousy told me by A, the Uranist
of whom we have already spoken. A, who has for long had
intimate relations with B, came to find him one day when
he had heard that B had received a visit from a Uranist C,
and had accepted gifts which the latter had offered. Upon
entering at B's, A, very much excited, asked him whether it
were true that he had accepted the gift from C. B said no.
Then A drawing a knife from his pocket said, "It's good for
you that you didn't accept the gift, for otherwise I would
have stabbed you with the knife which I have brought with
me for that purpose." A who is very impressionable affirms
that some day his jealousy will certainly force him to murder.

This condition of morbid over-excitation following a fit of
jealousy may be encountered among individuals who are
otherwise very honorable and honest. The blind passion of
the Uranist as well as that of the normal man can push them
both to crime. Euripedes rightfully makes Helan say in "The
Trojans":

> Whose power surpasses that of other gods,
> Is subdued and vanquished by love.
>   —Jupiter,

The following scene shows how far the jealousy of the
Uranists may go:

D has sexual intercourse with E. When D accompanies
E to his door and when the latter does not wish D to go

further, D suspects E of waiting for another man. He therefore remains all night to watch E's house to see whether anyone does come to him. On the other hand, when D wishes to absent himself, he has to take all the precautions possible so as not to awaken suspicions in E. If D talks ever so little with another man, E is convinced that the latter is a Uranist who wants to take his friend from him; he then causes a scene, in which his jealousy forces him to extract a promise from D not to see the same man again.

Another Uranist, F, who has intercourse with G readily looks at other men; G, who is very jealous, often boxes him on the ears for it, but F maintains that the blows he receives are pleasant because they show him that G loves him. In his "Anthropologie in Pragmatischer Hinsicht" Kant relates analogous facts in love: The ancient Russian legend ordinarily regarded as a fable declares that women who are not beaten from time to time believe that their husbands are not faithful to them. Cooke relates in his voyages that one day an English sailor, seeing an Indian beat his wife, told him to leave her alone. Whereupon the woman began to hurl invectives at the sailor, telling him that it was none of his business, etc.

Besides impassioned love, the jealousy of the Uranists is also explained by the nervous disposition of these individuals. The idea that the man he loves is deceiving him may become for the Uranist a veritable persecution complex which becomes more and more rooted in him, depriving him of his appetite, his sleep, and robbing him of his taste for travel. I know a case in which jealousy altered the character of a Uranist to such an extent that his family feared the beginning of a mental malady. Tarnowsky maintains that the jealousy of a Uranist who evinces an unhappy love for a normal man shows itself towards the women whom he considers as his rivals. Many Uranists who find themselves attracted to normal men experience sexual aversion for other Uranists.

The normal man does not love all women in the same manner. If his love is profound he feels himself attracted to some woman with whom he has relations, sometimes passing, sometimes durable, as in marriage, for example. The same phenomenon exists in the Uranist who very often feels himself peculiarly attracted by a class of men or by a single individual for whom he preserves his passion for years. It even appears to me that Uranists are much more spirited than normal men. In the normal man the passion for a woman can render him impotent towards all other women; the same phenomenon sometimes exist in the Uranist. However, a great many Uranists are rather polygamous: they have relations sometimes with one man, sometimes with another and do not attach themselves for a long time to the same individual. On the other hand, the monogamous Uranist remains a long time with his "acquaintance" whom he deceives, however, rather willingly when the occasion presents itself. A great many of them cannot have sexual intercourse with other Uranists. I was told that the Uranists know this quite well so that they are often obliged in order to avoid disgusting the man they love to hide their tendencies from him. Frequently a Uranist has relations with men in whom he does recognize the same tendencies as his own; but the moment he perceives his error, whether he makes the discovery of his own accord or whether the man discloses his character to him, immediately all further sexual contact becomes impossible for him. It must be admitted that it is the idea, the representation of man, which excites the Uranist; so that as soon as he perceives the effeminate nature of the man he loves—and the Uranist is in realty nothing else but a woman —all excitation ceases.

It is my impression that the majority of Uranists prefer to have sexual intercourse with normal men. A Uranist confessed to me that he felt himself attracted to men who make love to woman but he never dared to propose to them. We have said that some Uranists cannot have sexual intercourse with their kind. These need normal men, and it is this fact that explains the recent development of the masculine prostitution in large cities. To show to what extent

Uranists feel themselves attracted toward virility it suffices to cite the fact that they prefer men who possess large virile members. Krafft-Ebing tells of a Uranist who from the beginning could not have relations with individuals having the same tendencies as himself unless they had erections.

The moral possession of the beloved and purely spiritual love are rarely sought by Uranists. But this occurs. The desire of the Uranist meets with considerable difficulties not only because of social ostracism but also because of the fact that the love of a Uranist for a normal man is not reciprocated. The impossibility of fulfilling their desire is for a great many Uranists a source of torment and despair. An old Uranist told me even when the thing appears impossible Uranists always continue to delude themselves and to hope to be loved some day by a normal man.

The question of age in the relations between Uranists has not been presented in its true light. Friedrich believes that among pederasts it is the older one who uses *membrum in anum* of the younger. But it is far from being proven. Both are often of the same age. The older sometimes plays the passive part in pederasty. The error comes from the fact that in Greece love was practiced between a man of a certain age and a boy, between teacher and pupil. However, there are to be found even among the ancient Greeks numerous exceptions to this rule. As we have seen in speaking of historic men of that country relations of the same kind often existed between young people. The same conditions are met with nowadays in lyceums and colleges and principally in boarding schools for young people. Nevertheless it appears that in Ancient Greece boys and young people were preferred. One must not misconstrue the meaning of the word "boy"; we use it as a translation of the Greek word *pais* designating a boy who is quite grown. There are numerous passages in Greek authors which inform that the best time for pederasty is the period between puberty and commencement of the growth of the beard; in other words, between the ages of thirteen and eighteen. It is not rare even today to meet

with Uranists who have the same tastes as the ancient
Greeks. A student whom I know loves boys between the
ages of fourteen and sixteen: he has an antipathy for bearded
men who cause him more physical repugnance than women.

The adult Uranist as a rule is attracted by matured men.
It appears that tastes change with ages: the ancient Greeks
loved boys but today boys play a less important role in pederasty. Krafft-Ebing emphasizes the fact that adult Uranists
never seduce young people while libertines do. But the case
is not general and it appears to me that here again anomalies
exist which are even more pathologic than abnormal sexual
sensations. Just as there are men who are attracted only
by little girls so there are Uranists who prefer to have contact
only with boys.

It is very curious that a great many Uranists are attracted
by older men as they grow older themselves; they need an
age-equality for their sexual satisfactions; a boy of eight goes
with another boy of eight, a Uranist of twenty finds pleasure
in a young man of twenty, and so on. But then there are
many who, when older, return to young boys. Boys, how-
ver often seek adults.

The inclinations of the Uranists vary. Thus, a mature individual, of the Christian faith, and very blond, loves only
Jewish boys not older than sixteen. Another Uranist loves
workmen only; another is attracted by men in rags; one
loves brunettes, the other blondes. A great many can have
contact only with bearded men. A Uranist has declared to
me that he prefers men who are full-bearded and it is nevertheless possible for him to have relations with men wearing
only mustaches but that he can find no satisfaction whatever in clean-shaven men.

We must also mention the Uranists' peculiar bent for military men, especially for those who serve in the cavalry—a
penchant which very unmistakably recalls that of certain
women for uniforms and epaulettes. In certain Uranists this
penchant is so marked that it is impossible for them to have
intercourse with civilians.

The manner in which the Uranist satisfies his desire in the sexual act varies with the individual. The type of satisfaction which each chooses depends upon several causes among which imitation and example play a large role. It has not yet been proven that Uranists prefer a certain kind of coition *(immisio in os,* for example) to simple contact. In the normal state the desire is directed towards coition by placing the penis in the vagina. But I believe that even here imitation and example influence the preference for some definite form for satisfying the sexual instinct. A man who had intercourse with a woman can content himself for a certain time with applying his member against the woman's body. Unfortunately it is very difficult to answer this question. At one time, I thought I could find the answer in a study of children brought up far from society and in a state approaching veritable savagery. But I could draw no conclusion whatsoever. These children manifested an anesthesia of the genital senses when they received certain intellectual culture and lived among men. I even believe that the manner in which Uranists seek to satisfy the sexual instinct varies according to time and place. Thus I am convinced that at the time Tardieu wrote his book pederasty was more widespread in Paris, now, in Berlin.

The following case will show through what phases a Uranist passed in the satisfaction of his sexual desires: X, fifty years old and a very well-known artist, began his habits at a very early age of childhood. The first sexual ideas came to him at the age of ten or eleven: a young man, Y, took his hand and first placed it in his trousers and then on his genital organs. The touching of Y's genitals, the hair of his body or even their contemplation provoked in X a voluptuous sensation. Later he experienced a constant desire to look at the genital organs of men without however fully realizing the significance of his sensations. When he became older, contact with a man's body caused him to have agreeable sensations without awaking other ideas. Later he loved to press his cheeks against those of his comrades and to lie on the

body of one of them.   So it continued until his twenty-sixth
year without his doing anything else and without his knowing that these contacts could produce an ejaculation in him.
It was only at this period that while lying in the same bed
with one of his friends he pressed his member against the
body of his friend and had an ejaculation followed by voluptuous sensations.   This fact opened X's eyes.   He had never
practiced masturbation; at night he had voluptuous dreams
in which men always figured and which were followed by
pollutions: during the day he had never had pollutions.   Up
to this time, X believed that he could not be satisfied otherwise.   The *immissio in anum* repelled him; *aprimere membrum*
caused him the greatest pleasure; his companion above and himself below.

From a physiological viewpoint, the same succession of
phenomena may be observed in the Uranist as in the normal
man: to wit, erection and ejaculation accompanied by voluptuous sensations.   I have been told, however, that certain
Uranists do not go beyond an erection.   As an example let
me recall the history I have just reported in which until the
twenty-fifth year of the individual in question, the erection
accompanied by agreeable sensations was the limit of his
sexual activities.   It is understood that erection does not
even have to be complete for the accomplishment of coition,
for often the member does not penetrate.   Be that as it may,
in the Uranist as in the normal man, the erection precedes
the ejaculation the physiological processes being the same.

It is generally admitted that among Uranists coition is
practiced by placing *membrum in anum*.   This type of coition
is also known as pederasty.   It should not be believed, however, that this mode is frequent.   Certain authors, Krafft-
Ebing for example, are even of the opinion that coition is
practiced in this way may be observed only in depraved men.
I do not think so, if I am to believe what has been told me.
I am certain that pederasty is to be met with still rather frequently in Berlin, without any depravity.   The pederasts
are more numerous among aristocrats than among the pro-

letariat. N. N. does not think so. He believes that pederasty is very rare among Uranists and is to be observed equally in all classes of society. I ought, however, to say that Uranists rarely seek to satisfy their passions in this manner. Nevertheless, the individual rarely seeks to place *membrum in rectum* in pederasty; on the contrary, the *immissio in anum* provokes the desired enjoyment in a great many Uranists, the passive Uranist having an ejaculation under these circumstances. Somewhat to disguise the repugnant side of the act, some Uranists perfume the anus; meanwhile anointing the member with oil so that it can easily penetrate; taking care lest any faeci adhere to the member. Sometimes the anus may be widened by an instrument for easier penetration. Often while A places his member in the anus of B, B will grasp the member of A, masturbating him until he ejaculates in the anus of B.

I believe the opinion of Tarnowsky erroneous that, in all cases of acquired pederasty, the erection is followed very quickly by ejaculation, so that the act lasts only a very short time. I maintain once again that this type of coition is very rare among Uranists. My contention could be questioned on the ground that most Uranists do not confess it because pederasty is punishable by law and because they fear being denounced to the authorities. This is no objection for Uranists have told me of other species of coition practiced by them which are just as reprehensible as pederasty.

Men who have a tendency towards passive pederasty have often masturbated since their youngest childhood; only, instead of rubbing the member they ordinarily introduce any object whatever into their anus or rectum. Pederasty often causes ulcerous growths in the rectum which are very important from a medico-legal point of view. In like manner, gonorrhea of the rectum can result from it.

We repeat that *immissio in anum* of an individual of the masculine sex is generally known in Germany as pederasty. In this act, one is active, the insertor; the other is passive, the receiver. Authorities clearly separate active pederasty from passive pederasty, for when such a relation exists between two individuals, one is always active the other always passive. Coffignon, who has made a very fine study of this question in Paris, is of this opinion, and believes that in homosexual love this relation is much more determined in men than in women. I believe that it is just as definite, if not more so in women than in men. The one who plays the passive role is often called *Cynedes,* this word is ecpecially used to designate those passive pederasts who pay. However, Mantegazza uses the word *Cinedi* to indicate active pederasts and he reserves the word *Patici* for the passive pederasts. I know several cases in which this separation of active from passive pederasts is not very definite and these exceptions are important. We have already seen that Uranists exploit the erection of another Uranist for their personal satisfaction. It would be wrong to believe with certain authors that the passive pederast is more effeminate than the active pederast and that his bearing toward the latter is always passive like a woman's. Here is an example which upholds my thesis: A Uranist, X, has relations with another Uranist, Y, playing in these relations a passive role; however X is active in the sense that he loves to place *membrum in os* while Y who places *membrum in anum* is quite passive. Y loves to have X place *membrum suum in os* and then has an ejaculation; and for this Y need not even touch his member.

It is therefore not surprising that in a great many cases only the passive pederast obtains satisfaction, the active pederast not going any further than the erection for the reason that the subsequent act no longer corresponds to the sensations and desires of the individual.

It may be said that a great number of Uranists remain passive during their sexual life. Ulrichs admits that Uranists love to be embraced rather than to embrace contrary to what takes place in normal man. I have already said that in a great many cases the type of satisfaction sought by the Uranist depends upon imitation and other analogous causes. This observation should not be generalized. I think that the tendency to passive pederasty in a great many cases is not due to imitation. I believe that the tendency for passive pederasty is favored by a peculiar predisposition of the individual. Perhaps this case has to do with a phenomenon analogous to that met with in flagellation of which we shall speak further on, and in which the blows on the buttocks provoke heterosexual genital excitation in man enabling him to accomplish the act of coition. The passive pederast besides his inclination for man has need of a certain irritation of the nerves in anus and rectum for complete satisfaction and which he obtains only through contact with another man.

Another species of coition which is much more frequent is the *immissio in os* of the beloved. This act may be accomplished in several ways. Some take the entire member *in os*, not even excluding the testes, in order to lick it with the tongue and lips; or the testes may not enter, the beloved embracing it with his hands.

In this also there are Uranists who prefer to play the passive role and who love only to take *membrum in os*, and who have not even the desire to place *membrum in anus*. The first of these acts suffices to cause them sexual excitement. Also, when one of these passive Uranists has intercourse with an active Uranist, the insertor, the act is pleasurable to both; sometimes orgasms and the subsequent ejaculations happen simultaneously in both. But it is not so when both prefer the active role. In certain Uranists to take *membrum in os* causes no excitation whatever; they only do it by way of reciprocation.

The ejaculation does not take place *in os* for most often the member is withdrawn when ejaculation begin. In some Uranists perversion goes so far as to bring about not only *immissio membri* but even *ejaculatio seminis in os*. An individual, occupying a rather high social standing, has even told me that his passion consists of swallowing *semen ejaculatum in os*. There are also cases in which the one who ejaculated *in os* wanted to swallow the semen. These cases are somewhat rare.

Let us say once again that *immissio in os* is infinitely more frequent than pederasty. The one who takes in the member is called fellator, a word met with before in Martial and which served in the ancients to indicate children and slaves brought up especially for this purpose. Tarnowsky thinks that the pederast becomes a fellator solely for the purpose of prolonging the act and enjoyment thereof. This is not tenable. One must rather say that there are Uranists who can be satisfied only in such fashion and in whom this act provokes from the beginning to end the keenest excitement.

In a great many cases coition is practiced in such a fashion that the member is placed between the legs of the beloved by the verb *enfesser*. Others simply lie, one alongside the other who places the member in some part of the body. It also happens that a Uranist ejaculates in the armpit of the beloved, the latter, further to augment to excitation moves his arm about. But the most frequent form of coition is mutual masturbation in which each Uranist hold the other's member with his hand until ejaculation. Masturbation is practiced either simultaneously, separately or in turn. Frequently excitation may be tense enough to cause him to ejaculate without contact properly so-called, or through a casual contact. Uranists practice mutual masturbation standing or lying; rarely sitting. In mutual masturbation or simple masturbation of A by B, sometimes the hand is anointed with vaseline or oil.

Certain Uranists are masturbated by normal men. This fact is particularly frequently found among masculine prostitutes of which we have already spoken. Here mutual masturbation does not occur since one of the two is a normal man who feels himself attracted to women and experiences no excitement in his contact with the Uranist. Certain Uranists seek to cause ejaculation in their companion likewise. They therefore apply to normal individuals whom they pay; but they oblige them before attempting coition to dress themselves as women.

A great many Uranists seek and find their satisfaction in solitary masturbation, especially when they are not successful in establishing relations with other men. This is principally the case with homosexuals living in small cities. Onanism is also explained by other causes, such as lack of money, fear of law, modesty, etc.

When a normal man gives himself to masturbation, he ordinarily thinks of a woman during the act; a Uranist evokes the image of the man he loves, in analogous conditions. To cause excitement Uranists often possess pictures and anatomic models of the genital organs of man, which for them are just as exciting as the image of a nude woman is for normal men.

A Uranist, whose history is reported by Krafft-Ebing, practiced masturbation in a very singular fashion. Since he could not find a lover he placed himself before a large mirror and masturbated while regarding his own image; but at the same time he thought how much more agreeable it would be to have a real lover. Another patient of Krafft-Ebing's used to say that at the age of thirteen he was able to take his own member *in os*, while bending down as far as possible and the act terminated in an ejaculation. According to N. N. a great many Uranists boast of being able to do this. I believe that this is only a species of bragging.

It should be known that the Uranist does not always seek to satisfy himself in the same way and he often varies the means. This is not at all surprising, since the purpose of normal coitus (i.e., reproduction) is in these conditions completely lacking. In a great number the manner of coition varies with the age.

Among the modes of sexual satisfaction, the most curious is that in which the contact of the member with the body of the other man is not necessary. Several have erection followed by ejaculations in simply embracing the man they love. There are even some for whom it suffices merely to touch the man they love to display all the physiological phenomena of sexual enjoyment. Finally, there are Uranists who have ejaculations merely by looking at the naked bodies of their beloved. In the last case, the view of the virile member of the beloved plays the important role.

The cases in which sexual satisfaction takes place without bodily contact properly so-called somewhat recalls the "ideal coition" described by Hammond which I affirm exists also in Berlin. There resides therein a singular process requiring great powers of the imagination. I have heard of a painter, X, whose sexual desires are satisfied in this way. This is what takes place: X is seated in front of a pretty woman, well dressed, and he imagines that he is about to have coition with her. This mental representation being added to the very real impression produced by the woman is so powerful that X has an erection and ejaculates without rubbing his member. This imaginary coition satisfies X better than a real coitus would.

Simple masturbation probably causes a complex of the genital system, needing only embracing, touching or even looking at a man to cause an erection and ejaculation. But these individuals do not find satisfaction in this act; they complain of experiencing enjoyment of little intensity.

It is just as difficult to estimate the frequency of sexual intercourse in the Uranist as it is in the normal man. Numerous variations are to be found according to the individuals; some because of an hyperesthesia often accomplish this act several times a day, others do it once every eight or fifteen days or even at longer periods. The same fact exists in Uranists as in normal men, namely, boasting and exaggerating regarding the frequency of intercourse. Between the two extremes there exist, of course, many intermediate cases.

It is difficult to say whether there are Uranists in whom the sexual life does not exist; that is to say, who do not practice masturbation and who no not have intercourse with men. I do not know of one case of this type among Uranists; the fact is however possible, since among normal men there are those who in the full flowering of their forces have not yet had intercourse with women nor have they practiced masturbation. The erotic dreams of the Uranists are always of men and are often accompanied, as in normal men, by seminal discharges and pleasure.

In almost all the cases of sexual inversion, the other member is the principle exciting element; it even seems that the virile member excites the Uranist more keenly than the genital organs of a woman excite a normal man. Thus a Uranist whom I know found so much voluptuous pleasure in it that at the age of ten he awoke one night, approached the bed of one of his comrades who slept in the same room and raised the cover so that he could contemplate at his leisure his naked friend. He then had a violent erection which was accompanied by voluptuous sensations. At the same time, he tried not to awaken his friend, and at the least warning ran to his bed in fear of being discovered.

Saulle has cited the case of a student who had an extraordinary desire for men and statues of naked men. His greatest enjoyment consisted in examining the penis of a man urinating next to him. It is evident that this Uranist was not excited by the act of urinating but by the sight of the member. Many Uranists experience voluptuous sensations not only while looking at the member of another man but also in showing him theirs. N. N. has drawn my attention to this point. It is difficult to say of what this voluptuousness consists. A great number of Uranists among my patients felt great enjoyment showing themselves entirely naked or showing only their genital organs to other Uranists and normal men. This very much recalls the exhibitionists who exhibit their genital organs before persons of the other sex. This is evidently a case which is not encountered often. In the public urinals one sometimes sees men hold the genital organs of those who are next to them. These places are particularly frequented by Uranists. Charcot and Magnan relate the case of an individual of this type who seated himself on a bench on a river bank to look at naked men who were bathing. He remained there under the pretext of sketching.

Uranists do not exclusively seek the sexual act, properly so-called; they experience equal pleasure in kissing and embracing. When they kiss each other it is with the same purpose as when a man and woman do it; the excitation produced by the contact of the tongues is the same in them as in normal men and women.

Chapter V

MALE PROSTITUTION

Male Versus Female Prostitution; Blackmailing of Inverts.

The need of satisfying normal sexual instincts has caused the development in society of a special class of women who sell their charms for money. Certain individuals have taken advantage of the homosexual tendencies of Uranists to form an analogous class recruited from men. The origin of masculine prostitution is very old. Aeschinus complained of pederasty in which a man prostituted himself for money; Hug cites a passage in Plato's "Banquet" which shows that in love the relations of the parties concerned greatly resemble those resulting from a bill of sale. In one of his elegies Tibullus complains of the faithlessness of a young boy to whom he had given gifts as the price of his favors. Today masculine prostitution is quite widespread, and we possess numerous documents relating to the trade in many of the large cities.

Among recent works may be cited that of Coffiignon who gives very valuable data concerning masculine prostitution in Paris. In that city male prostitutes known as *petits-jesus* exploit hotels where rich foreigners stop and where

109

they seek positions as grooms. After some time the groom in question succeeds in creating a certain clientele. At times the clients come to Paris in the company of the groom to satisfy their passions. According to a patient of Krafft-Ebing masculine prostitution exists in all the large cities.

Male prostitutes almost always have a definite place where they meet. In Berlin there is a resort where one may find at any time fifty of these immoral individuals. Moreover there are in Berlin well-known places, a sort of market, where these individuals offer themselves to the Uranists. These transactions also take place in public lavatories. At one time there existed in Berlin a sort of male brothel where an elderly man acted as overseer. Blackmail played a great part in the prospering of this house. The majority of the members of the masculine underworld are not Uranists. Still there are certainly a great many homosexuals who receive money for their favors. Beside these, there are normal men who are sometimes even married. They make use of their relations with men to enrich themselves.

Although the masculine prostitutes are quite normal sexually they sometimes assume the appearance and carriage of women. In order to recognize each other they paint and powder, wear gaudy costumes, etc. According to Krauss the Cynedes of ancient Greece dressed as women wearing their hair in braids, etc., in order to attract men. I do not understand why heterosexual prostitutes imitate the effeminate carriage of the Uranists. The reason for this is probably the desire to attract the attention of the Uranists; however, most Uranists prefer men presenting all the masculine characteristics. There may be some who seek men dressed as women. Here it is most profitable to remain young a long time. Probably this is another reason why a male prostitute, just like a girl, has recourse to the artifices of the toilette. The age of these individuals ordinarily range from seventeen to thirty, but there are some who are older and some younger. It is scandalous that among them are to be found young boys, almost children.

Outside of the immoral phase of masculine prostitution, there is a peculiar type who is supported by another who in turn finds the money necessary for his love affairs by prostituting himself to other men. There also exists among the masculine underworld certain celebrities who travel from city to city, from country to country, always receiving acclaim. One sometimes finds certain individuals who are the apex about which a group revolves. Sometimes one of them is supported by a rich Uranist who provides him with a house, luxuries and with all the pleasures of life on condition that he reserve his favors for him alone. The masculine underworld greatly resembles the feminine underworld. All that characterizes one is to be found in the other. Very often a member of the masculine underworld will lower his price to eclipse his comrades in the number of his trade. Others are vain about their relations with men of high position, and it is with pride that—and in this they very much resemble women —they boast of their relations with a prince or a count.

Like women these men are very importunate and very bold. They employ any means to attract the attention of the Uranists before giving themselves. They try to get as much money as possible out of their client and by making him drunk they sometimes succeed in robbing him. Some Uranists try to humble their companions by spreading the news that they sell their favors. A great many who have relations with others only for money deny it in order to raise themselves in the estimation of their companions. In general it seems that masculine prostitution has increased markedly during the last decade. A Uranist who has been acquainted with this trade for quite a while complains that it is today entirely commercialized and that the love element has disappeared. Masculine prostitution is one of the saddest phases of our customs and it is to be regretted that the police do not concern themselves with it as they do with its feminine counterpart. In treating this question from a judicial standpoint, I shall return to the fact that the police though armed against feminine prostitution are powerless in dealing with masculine prostitution.

There are certain cases in which men dressed as women are impudent enough to give themselves to men without causing the latter to suspect that they are having intercourse with individuals of the masculine sex. The cases cited by Froenkel and Westphals are very striking examples. A patient confessed to Krafft-Ebing of knowing a young man who dressed as a woman and gave himself to men, making them believe that they were having an affair with a woman. He ordinarily told them that there were moral rules by which he abided and for this reason he could satisfy them only *per os.*

Masculine prostitution resembles the feminine in still another way. These individuals, like prostitutes, do not hesitate robbing their clients when the occasion presents itself and theft is even more frequent among male than among female prostitutes. This is not surprising when one is conscious of the fact that the victim of the theft would hesitate in bringing a complaint against a man even more than he would against a woman. Masculine prostitutes often follow their calling in order to steal from their clients. The latter can do nothing against them for fear of the intervention of the law in their affairs and the publishing of their unnatural passion. That would be their moral ruin. Uranists feel this so keenly that masculine prostitutes do not hesitate practicing methodic blackmail. The leader of the blackmailers forces the Uranist by his menaces to pay him for his silence. This procedure has been sufficiently brought to light in trials which have taken place in Berlin and in other large cities. A police agent, in speaking of one of these young captains of extortion told me, "I don't believe he is a sexual invert; rather, I think that he practices pederasty for money. When he happens upon a timid Uranist extortion begins. He threatens to denounce him as depraved. The Uranist therefore seeks to buy the silence of the blackmailer, which is not always an easy thing to do for when he has paid, the other repeats his threat. So it goes on endlessly." The blackmail sometimes leads the Uranist to suicide; in other cases, he clears himself with a considerable sum. Thirty thousand dollars, for example, in a case I know.

For the Uranist blackmail is a veritable sword of Damocles. Nowadays the courts often have to judge cases concerned with the outraging of moral customs in which extortion plays a large role. In those cases in which Uranists are brought to justice they naturally do not reproach themselves with those acts that are suppressed by the Penal Code. They usually confess only to mutual masturbation which does not come under the application of the law because of the absence of witnesses. But it is quite otherwise when the Uranist sues the blackmailer. The best thing he could do in this case is to inform the police from the beginning of the entire affair. For otherwise he risks being entirely deprived of what he has and after having the affair brought to court the only course left him is suicide. It is not to be believed that blackmail is practiced only by masculine prostitutes. There are men who apparently give themselves to Uranists purely for love; but later they appear and practice blackmail as a matter of form. Even when the Uranist has given all he has the blackmailer still does not let him go. He always lies in wait for him and when his victim succeeds in earning a few dollars he returns to his prey. The Uranist thus passes his life in perpetual fear and finishes by losing his social position.

The means employed by successful extortionists vary considerably. Let us suppose, for example, that A performs with a man, B, a sexual act which falls under the application of the law. A believes that he is alone with B, but all of a sudden during the act a third person, C, appears who plays the role of the person wronged and who threatens to report the whole affair to the police. C and B are evidently accomplices, but C acts as though he were going to denounce B as well as A. B then tries to allay C's anger by offering him money, etc., which leads A to make the same propositions. The two accomplices are quite well aware of A's identity, and if they do not know it they follow their victim to his house to identify him. There are also hired plotters among the blackmailers who seek to attract the attention of the Uranists towards them and to place them in a position to accomplish the sexual act; then the extortion immediately begins.

If one thinks that blackmail, which constitutes a veritable plague, depends upon the law against the outragers of natural functions one has a right to ask oneself whether that law is or is not detrimental rather than useful. I shall return to this question. In all cases, one cannot too highly praise the severity of the courts in dealing with extortionitsts. Blackmailers do not always threaten their victims with betrayal to the courts, an action which would bring them little gain. In certain cases they threaten their victims with a public revelation of their passion, either by causing a street scene or by gossiping among his friends and acquaintances. The blackmailer knows full well that because of the contempt which the Uranist encounters everywhere, his revelation would cause his victim to be ostracised by all of society. However Uranists do not ordinarily dare to threaten with blackmail those individuals who have never had intercourse with men and who are perfectly normal sexually.

Chapter VI

SEXUAL PERVERSION AS A COMPLICATION OF SEXUAL INVERSION

Object Fetichism; Fetichistic Histories; Body Fetichism; Masochism; Desire to Be Humiliated; Sadism; Gilles De Rayes; A Case of Inverted Masochism; Case Continued; Intercourse with Boys; Inversion and Perversion.

A full understanding of Uranism is possible only by comparing sexual perversions which develop in this field with those which one encounters in heterosexual love. It is curious that in sexual inversion which draws man to man there are to be found the same perversions as exist in certain sexual relations between man and woman. We owe the knowledge of these very interesting facts principally to Krafft-Ebing's numerous works.

In the normal state the genital organs of the woman cause the major excitation in man, and coition is the principal means of satisfying the sexual instinct. But it is not always so. There are men who are excited by a part of the female body other than the genital organs, or even by a part of her costume. With Lombroso, Binet and Dessoir, Krafft-Ebing called this particular state fetichism. We can consequently distinguish between fetichism directed to an object or part of the dress and fetichism directed to part of the body. This

distinction is all the more justified since in certain of these
individuals fetichism is directed, for example, to shod feet;
the nude feet of a woman being of no interest whatsoever to
them.   Others, on the contrary, find their fetish in bare
hands; gloved hands leaving them completely cold.

The cases of fetichism of objects are very numerous.   It
is a known fact that often, when one loves a woman, one
covers with kisses those objects which belong to her, her
gloves, her letters, etc.   The Poles observe the custom of
drinking wine from the boots of their women.   All these cases
are evidently quite analogous to fetichism.   One must not
however consider as morbid the habit of embracing the objects belonging to the beloved person, lest one attribute a
temporary or chronic sexual perversion to all men.

What distinguishes normal from morbid cases is that in the
first there is a love for a person, and that if one embraces the
objects of the woman beloved, it is exactly because they belong to the loved one.   In pathological fetichism the love of
the object is the prime factor.   The physical and moral qualities of the person in question is more or less appreciated by
these patients, but they are always forced to the background.
Shoe-fetichism as described by Zola in "Therese Raquen," in
which the man embraces the elegant shoe of the beloved
woman is an example of normal fetichism, since the man, at
the same time, seeks passionately to have sexual intercourse
with the loved one.   On the contrary, those cases of fetichism
are morbid in which coition is not sought but in which all
desires tend towards the sensual idolatry of some part of a
dress or of some object.   It is immaterial from a pathological
viewpoint whether the object belongs to an acquaintance or
whether the fetichist uses the object to call up an imaginary
person; whether the fetichist contents himself with admiring,
feeling, or covering the woman's shoe with kisses or whether
he uses it as a pretext for masturbation.

In object-fetichism the principal role is played by the shoes
and linen of a woman, her handkerchief, for example.   There
are a series of cases of criminal significance in which men

appropriate the handkerchiefs and lingerie of women. The passion for handkerchiefs may be so violent that the man finds himself completely conquered by them. A lady told me: "I know a gentleman; all I have to do when I see him from afar is to draw from my pocket a corner of my handkerchief to make him follow me like a dog. No matter where I go he does not leave me. Whether this gentleman is riding or occupied in very serious and very important affairs, as soon as he sees my handkerchief he leaves everything to follow me, or rather, to follow my handkerchief." This handkerchief-fetichism is used in many ways to satisfy the sexual instinct. Some content themselves with stealing women's handkerchiefs, carrying them home, and enjoying the good fortune of possessing a collection of them. Law courts, which often have to deal with the theft of handkerchiefs, proceed today with great prudence. In other fetichists possession of the handkerchief alone is not sufficient to cause genital excitation: they need something else. I know a fetichist who only by tearing the woman's handkerchief with his teeth can experience sexual enjoyment. In a case published by Dietz the patient had an ejaculation only when he tore the lingerie of a woman with his teeth.

Handkerchief fetichism exists also among Uranists. Just as the fetichist of women's handkerchiefs finds no satisfaction in cotion, the Uranist fetichist obtains enjoyment only in men's handkerchiefs. The fetichists of this type are excited neither by pederasty nor by mutual masturbation. The genitals of man do not at all attract them—just as the female genitals have no exciting influence upon the fetichists of female handkerchiefs. The following is an example which shows the means employed by Uranist-fetichists to satisfy their passion. It deals with a vigorous worker, X, forty years of age. He is well built. He consulted me on his troubles which were of a neurasthenic and hypochondriacal origin: headaches, weariness in the legs, lack of will to work, pain in the back, etc. After having been for some time under my treatment he told me one day of his sexual life.

He was never attracted to women; on the contrary, handsome men excited him in quite an unusual manner. He had never practiced pederasty nor mutual masturbation but, on the other hand, he was often given to solitary onanism. His greatest enjoyment consisted in stealing the linen or the handkerchiefs of good-looking men, of enveloping his penis therein and masturbating. He often used the handkerchiefs of his friends for this purpose and to avoid any suspicion of theft would leave one of his own handkerchiefs in the place of the one stolen in order to create the impression that it had happened accidentally. When he had no handkerchief at his disposal he would, while masturbating, evoke the image of a handkerchief or of another article of men's linen. He often had coition with female prostitutes but almost always without experiencing great satisfaction or enjoyment. He could not have an erection or an ejaculation under these conditions unless he thought of a man's handkerchief. He accomplished coition more easily if he held a friend's handkerchief in his hand during the entire act. The patient's erotic dreams dealt with neither coition nor the female genitals but with men's linen, causing ejaculation.

Women's foot-wear as well as lingerie may become the object of fetichism in man. The same fact exists likewise among men. I know an educated man in a responsible position who pestered an officer with letters in which he asked permission to polish his boots. The man who, according to a competent observer, was an out-and-out Uranist wrote these letters in quite a passionate tone, and forced the officer to seek the aid of the authorities to rid him of his correspondent.

It is curious that most Uranists consider with scorn fetichism and all other sexual perversions except pure sexual inversion. One has told me, for example, that he regards the passion for shoes with contempt, but that he understands homosexual love quite well and considers it quite moral.

Entirely different from the cases of object-fetichism cited in which coition is not sought despite the heterosexual desire, there are cases in which coition is the aim. The only difference is that the desire and the possibility of accomplishing coition depend expressly on some article of dress, or some toilette. It must be here decided whether or not the presence of a certain article of dress is indispensable for genital excitation before or during coition. But the facts we possess on the subject are not sufficiently numerous to permit the easy separation of those two classes of facts. Several examples will serve to throw light on this point.

A, twenty-six years old, told me that he could not have intercourse with an entirely nude woman: she must at least wear her chemise. Another man experienced genital excitement only when the woman wore white bloomers. Still another told me of certain feminine costumes which could cause him great excitement. He described them thus: "The woman must wear either a short cloth jacket, or a long very dark mantle; the waist must be very tight and of a very dark color; the skirt, equally dark, must not have many pleats." This man also required women to wear elegant boots, long stockings, white bloomers and a chemise of the same color. He always chooses women dressed in this fashion for coition. C especially loves velvet. He experiences a normal urge for women but he becomes very excited when the woman with whom he has intercourse wears a velvet costume: his excitement is caused, not by looking at, but by feeling the velvet. Still another, a doctor by profession, has told me that he is excited at the sight of ladies' polished shoes; he is also excited by a tightly fitted figure and a mantle very wide at the hips. Cases of this kind in which the sexual urge leads to coition appear to me to be quite frequent. And yet a great many of them may be classed as pathological. To be able to distinguish them one must always ask oneself the following question: Is or is not such and such an article of dress or its simple mental image the *sine qua non* of genital excitation? If it is, the case is pathological like that of the individual who could perform coition only when the woman wore her chemise. If on the other hand such and such an article of dress only augments the genital excitation the case must be considered normal. The difficulties of classification from the viewpoint of the woman's dress may be avoided in this manner.

The same phenomena also exist in homosexual love. Here, likewise, the costume exercises a considerable influence over the awaking and excitation of the sexual urge. I know a Uranist who can have intercourse with another man only when the latter wears polished ladies' shoes and black stockings. The sexual act itself is mutual masturbation. The preference of Uranists for soldiers is thus partly explained. It is a known fact that the same thing is true of women, but until now there was no adequate explanation of the attraction exercised over women by the military uniform. Perhaps it is the idea of courage and decision intimately bound up with uniforms that seduces the woman. It may exist unconsciously according to the psychological mechanism concerned even while exercising the action in question. Perhaps the same causes play a part in the Uranists love for soldiers, even for the uniform. There are always Uranists who have intercourse only with soldiers. Finally we must cite in this special category those Uranists who have intercourse with men dressed as women. This is not prevalent, as we have already said, but there are Uranists who are cold to men wearing the masculine costume and who become excited by those dressed as women.

Let me also speak here of those Uranists who are not excited by naked men. These cases are rare but they exist. The following is what a Uranist writes on the subject: "Curiously enough, I am excited only by men who are dressed. The entirely naked men one sees in Roman or Russian baths leave me entirely indifferent and awaken in me, at most, a purely esthetic sentiment!" In heterosexual love the desire for women entirely or partly dressed and the aversion for nude women is not infrequent. Cases of this type have been published by Hammond, Krafft-Ebing and others. I know a husband who can have intercourse with his wife only when she is dressed in a certain way. In this group of object-fetichism, there also enter those cases in which the woman must wear certain cloths, such as silk, velvet, fur, etc.

I have said that beside object fetichism there is a fetichism of parts of the body. In this case the Uranist is no longer excited by the handkerchief or the shoe of the man he loves, but by a part of the body which becomes the object of the Uranist's love. The genital organs therefore play a more subordinate role in all these cases than in the case of the ordinary Uranist. Man's foot is the principal object of fetichism of the Uranist and this fact exists likewise in heterosexual love.

The pathologic form of fetichism of the parts of the body presents in heterosexual love numerous transitions leading to simple preference for certain parts of the body particularly beautiful or well-developed. Blond hair is preferred by one, small hands by another, a pretty mouth by a third. Novelists have utilized a great many observations of this kind in their novels.

I also consider in object-fetichism those cases in which the desires are satisfied not by coition *per vaginam* but by another act, such as masturbation with the hand or foot, coition *inter mammas,* etc., as pathologic. I do not consider pathologic those cases in which there is experienced a particular pleasure in regarding, touching, covering with kisses some parts of the body. These cases are perhaps to be considered abnormal, although not morbid. If one were to consider these cases pathological one would run the great risk of confusing the normal with the abnormal state, men's tastes being quite variable in this direction. One loves a pretty mouth, another blond hair or brown, a third large eyes, a fourth small feet. The following examples show how certain parts of the body may excite some individual.

A physician, who never showed the least sign of sexual perversion, told me that he is particularly excited by a woman's arms but at the same time, the final desire is coition *per vaginam.* However he vigorously grasps and kisses the woman's arms during coition. Another individual, an artist

by profession, is excited by the nape of the neck and especially by that part of the neck where the hair commences to
grow. Guy de Maupassant, the celebrated French realist, considers that spot quite particularly made for kisses. A third
individual feels violent genital excitement the moment he perceives a woman with braided hair; hair that is not braided
causes him no excitement whatsoever, no matter how beautiful it may be. The same individual has a very marked preference for ears. But to excite him, the ears must be small
and close to the head, the lobes unpierced and without ear-
rings. Within certain limits such cases of fetichism have
nothing in common with morbid sexual perversion. But this
limit is difficult to determine precisely for we still possess too
little material relative to fetichism in love. I believe that
those cases in which the sexual perception of a certain part
of the body or its mental representation is the *sine qua non* of
the voluptuous excitation may be considered pathological.
In these cases the woman insofar as she is feminine can not
alone cause the excitation. One may say that in pathologic
cases the woman is a sort of accessory to that part of the
body which plays the principal role in exciting the man.

Fetichism of parts of the body exist in homosexuals as well
as in heterosexuals. In homosexual love the feet of the beloved may also be the fetich. An individual, for example,
feels quite a peculiar, voluptuous sensation while kissing a
young man's toes, and this sensation causes an ejaculation.
Kissing the feet of the loved man is an act frequently performed among Uranists. Some also prefer feet that perspire,
while others have a horror of feet covered with perspiration.
A Uranist told me that he felt a violent sexual excitement on
getting into a boat and looking at the boatman's feet. Some
have told me that they are violently excited at the sight of
men's thighs forced into very tight trousers. Tarnowsky
proved that individuals subject to sexual inversion are greatly
excited by the buttocks and anuses of men. Albert published
several observations about school masters who whip their
pupils, the sight of the uncovered part of the body causing

them extreme excitement. Perhaps in these phenomena we must take into account not only the simple contemplation of a part of a body but also the consciousness of causing pain by whipping—a fact to which we shall return in speaking of sadism. Tarnowsky's opinion that those who feel attracted to men's buttocks are active pederasts does not appear to me to be true. I know men for whom men's buttocks exercise a peculiar attraction: they love to press and touch them feeling great sexual excitement; but it is impossible for them, through disgust, *membrum ittittere in anum*. It is equally untrue that men of this category have no feminine tendencies, as it is maintained by Tarnowsky, and this error is due to the general though inexact division of Uranists into active and passive.

Besides fetichism there is also to be encountered in homosexual love the phenomenon known as masochism, of which we owe the acquaintance and even the explanation to Krafft-Ebing. The word comes from the celebrated novelist Sacher-Masoch who in his novels especially applies himself to depicting men whose greatest joy is in feeling themselves subjugated and even maltreated by women. This phenomenon manifests itself in the desire to be beaten by the beloved person. However Krafft-Ebing considers the masochistic tendencies in man as a perversion having much in common with sexual inversion. He particularly admits that the phenomenon of submission is psychologically normal in woman's love, while in man it is the desire to dominate that is normal. On the contrary when it is the man who seeks to submit we are dealing, according to Krafft-Ebing, with a particular form of sexual inversion in the sense that one must consider as morbid the existence in man of a phenomenon which normally should exist in woman. I approve on the whole of this ingenious idea which however is not beyond certain objections. Moreover this conception of Krafft-Ebing's had been formulated before by Ramdohr. It is a known fact that J. J. Rousseau experienced genital excitation only when beaten by the woman he loved. Ramdohr in analyzing the loves of

Jean-Jacques arrived at the conclusion that he loved and felt like a woman. He always preferred to play the passive part.

Masochism has always existed and during certain epochs it was an epidemic. One of Krafft-Ebing's patients includes the Middle Ages among these epochs, with its courtesans and its cavaliers submitted to their ladies like veritable slaves, In a lesser degree the same phenomenon existed in the Rome of the Caesars, according to the poets and other writers of that period. Ramdohr insists that in the elegies of the poets of that period, the beloved woman is made to appear as the mistress and the amorous man as a slave in irons.

The submission of one person to another may be psychic or symbolic or it may assume a physical character. Krafft-Ebing rightfully insists that the ability of certain persons to become sexually excited only by experiencing pain is quite analogous to masochism; it has even been given a very determined form. In heterosexuals it may often be observed in a form of flagellation, the desire to be beaten with a rod by the beloved woman; in all these cases flaggellation on the buttocks plays the principal role.

The same phenomenon is to be met with among homosexuals. A Uranist whom I know often desires to be beaten by his companion and to gain his ends arouses his jealousy. "A little jealous scene," he told me, "caused my lover to become quite excited, and he would finally beat me. But when the blows came from him, they give me great enjoyment. I sometimes faint while he beats me." Another Uranist has sent me his autobiography which I cite here from the standpoint of masochism. "The mental images which I have while I masturbate are of a sexual nature. At the age of ten or twelve I thought of myself submitting to a man who excited me in many ways; later, when I was taller, the role I imagined myself playing in the sexual act was always that of a woman. Kisses on the arms and on the whole body were given in an exciting manner; but above all I experienced the desire to be beaten on the buttocks by the man I loved. I believe I submitted to all this with voluptuousness. I would have been happy to have received these blows and I would certainly have ejaculated. It is a servile submission to the man who is loved, going as far as complete sacrifice of dignity and marching hand in hand with a limitless fantasy." Another Uranist has complete satisfaction and ejaculation only when the man with whom he has intercourse rubs his back with a brush until the blood comes; this act is indispensable to his enjoyment.

Krafft-Ebing groups with masochism a certain number of other phenomena also. Certain repugnant acts springing from the desire to be humiliated and debased accompany masochism. Among the data of this type the most repugnant communicated to me concerns a Uranist whose greatest passion consisted in kissing the anus. In accomplishing this act the Uranist, a man of fifty years, has an erection and ejaculates. There are men who while seeking sexual intercourse with women have entire satisfaction only when they drink a woman's urine. This is sometimes met with in homosexuals and there are Uranists who have complete sexual satisfaction only when the other urinates *in os*. The passive Uranist can ejaculate only under this condition.

Krafft-Ebing attributes a great many cases of fetichism to masochism. Thus for him fetichism of shoes and of feet has a purely symbolic idea as origin. Indeed to be kicked means to be humiliated, and as we have already seen, the Uranist is dominated by this desire to debase his own personality. Krafft-Ebing supposes that although the shoe-fetichist is not conscious of the fact himself, this relation between the love of the boot and the wish for personal humiliation is quite real and is the source of fetichism, the unconscious desire to debase oneself before women. A great many facts favor this hypothesis. For example, I know a man who is a masochist and a shoe-fetichist at the same time: he is as easily excited sexually by a shoe as by the sentiment of being humiliated by a woman. Thus certain cases of fetichism may be connected with masochism.

However, I think that Krafft-Ebing's opinion is not entirely beyond objection. It is always difficult to explain, for example, why the fetichist connects his passion with high-heeled, buttoned or polished shoes. If one considers the close relation which in certain pathologic conditions unites the sense of smell with the sexual instinct one could believe that shoe-fetichism must perhaps be explained by the strong odor which adheres to the feet or to shoes.

In conclusion, we may say that Tardieu published an observation in which a man found enjoyment when another stepped on his toes. According to the same author, certain pederasts knelt before dirty children and passionately kiss their feet. Finally, let us cite the masochistic tendencies of Nero who invented the following game: He had the skin of a wild beast sewed about him and thus arrayed threw himself upon the genitals of men and women attached to a stake. When this savage passion was satisfied he allowed himself, according to Suetonius, to be possessed by Doryphorus, his freed man. It was Doryphorus who played the part of the husband, just as Sporus had played the part of woman before, and during "coitus" Nero imitated the cries of a virgin being raped.

There also exists a peculiar form of sexual perversion to be found in heterosexuals as well as in homosexuals and which has not yet been described. I believe it could be called mixoscopy (from *mixis*—sexual union and *scopein*—to look at). In heterosexuals there are men who find their satisfaction not in coition with a woman but in watching another man practicing coition. There is probably a certain connection between this phenomenon and masochism. The excitement may be caused by the pain of seeing the woman's being possessed by a third, and I know several cases of individuals who experience genital excitement only by this means. The same phenomenon is to be observed among homosexuals. Tarnowsky has published a case of very great interest. It deals with two boys who were taught by a man to masturbate. The latter contented himself with looking at them and he intervened sometimes but only as a pederast. This state took possession of the individual in question only periodically. Finding satisfaction in the pederasty of others should always be considered as pathologic. On the island of Capri, the Emperor Tiberius also contented himself with witnessing the sexual acts of young people and it was only in this way that he could become sexually excited.

Besides masochism, there is sadism to be studied, which is the direct opposite of masochism and is characterized by the fact that the sexual urge manifests itself in a desire to beat, to maltreat and to humiliate the beloved one. The word sadism comes from the name of a famous French novelist, the Marquis de Sade (1740-1814) who was condemned to death for sodomy, poisoning and other crimes, and who wrote novels in prison in which he established a close connection between voluptuousness and cruelty. A great many authors have already insisted on a connection between voluptuousness and pain, and have maintained that what is painful for one, may be, under pathologic conditions, a source of enjoyment for another. There are numerous examples which show that the victim's pain causes voluptuous sensations in the sadist. But what truly characterized sadism is the close connection between the need of tormenting and the genital functions. Consequently one should impute a cruel and brutal action to sadism only when it would constitute an excitation indispensable to the accomplishment of the latter. In normal love one may also find certain facts constituting a very attenuated form of sadism like the pleasure that the person who loves may find in causing the loved one chagrin by mocking and teasing her.

The acts of cruelty which the sadist may commit under pathologic conditions against a woman, and which procure sexual satisfaction for him may consist in beating, wounding, or soiling her in a thousand ways, in binding or even killing her which is known as a passionate murder. It is probable moreover that rape is often caused by sadistic tendencies. Thus, Krafft-Ebing reports the very interesting case of a man in whom coition had caused voluptuous sensations only once:

and that was when he raped a young girl. When the same young girl later assented to coition the man no longer experienced any enjoyment.

It is difficult to say exactly whether certain historic facts ought to be attributed to sexual perversion in general or to sadism in particular. It is certain however that a great many historic cruelties have no other origin. When one reads the life of Ivan the Terrible, one involuntarily gets the idea that the cruelty of this terrible and inhuman tyrant was caused by sexual perversion. His son Dimitri experienced peculiar joy in watching the convulsions and the blood of sheep, chickens, geese that were killed in his presence. It is a known fact that the same phenomenon exists even today in certain sexual perverts who have erections and even ejaculations when they see chickens and geese killed before them.

In the physiological state there exist in coition certain phenomena which recall sadism, although the conscious desire to cause pain may be absent. In this category of facts may be cited the actions of squeezing and violently embracing during coition. One of the parties may bite till the blood flows when he completely forgets in his voluptuous ecstasy the existence of the other party. The same phenomenon also exists among Uranists and I know one who carries on his body traces of assaults of this type. However I do not know of a case of very pronounced sadism among homosexuals. I have been told of a Uranist who found enjoyment in maltreating the man he loved: but the person in question denied the fact and would not even confess his Uranistic tendencies, which were well known.

There have been published some acts of sadism based on homosexuality. One case which belongs to this category has been published by Gyurkovechky. It dealt with a boy of fifteen, A, who had a friend, B, of fourteen. The mother of the latter had noticed that he bore bruises on his arms, back and thighs. It was learned that B had been paid by A to allow himself to be forcefully pinched by him. When B cried and wept with pain, A continued to pinch him with one hand and masturbated with the other. When questioned, A confessed that masturbating while B cried caused him the greatest enjoyment. A was epileptic and possessed a very nervous heredity. Other cases have been published of sadism in homosexuals; they deal with boys submitted to all sorts of acts, mutilation, etc. The case of von Zastrow was reported by Ulrichs in his "Incubus." Zastrow sought young boys and was prosecuted in the courts for all sorts of acts which he had inflicted on them: bites on the face, wounds, tearing out of the testicles, etc.

Ulrichs has brought together in his book other cases of sadism noticed among homosexuals. He particularly cites the schoolmaster J. Pellanda of Landsberg who had such a passion for boys that he would bite their cheeks until the blood ran. He also reports the history of a Uranist who became delirious during the sexual act when the man with whom he had intercourse and whom he maltreated during coition twisted with pain. In addition he recalls the words of von Gorres who said that sexual desire is the brother of the assassin, and he mentioned on this occasion the Marquis de Sade, celebrated for his cruelty to boys and girls.

Two historic facts show sadism in homosexuals. After having made men drink wine in large quantities, Tiberius had their members tied so as to cause them violent suffering due to the retention of urine as well as the tightness of the bonds. The other fact took place in the Middle Ages. It deals with a remarkable law suit which was held in 1440, under the reign of Charles VII, King of France. A French marshal, Gilles de Rayes, had violated and killed a considerable number of children, among whom were many boys. He was condemned and beheaded in 1440. It is very curious to note that Gilles de Rayes was brought to commit these atrocities through the reading, as he maintained, of Suetonious who described the sexual perversions of the Roman emperors.

I wish to cite here another case, very curious in its kind. It has occupied the attention of police and it is due to their kindness that I have heard about it. According to the discussion of the trial which took place, one cannot say whether it concerned merely an unpleasant joke or whether it really dealt with a morbid perversion. Whatever it was, the case is very interesting. It deals with a gentleman, A, a sexual pervert who living abroad had engaged a domestic, B, without knowing him. A rented a villa in the provinces and sent this domestic there, while he himself remained abroad and wrote him instructions according to which he should receive a certain C and force him to indulge in pederasty. C, according to a letter from A to B, had to go to the villa, bearing a letter from A, and B had to do with C what A would tell him. These instructions sent by A to B are stamped with such cynicism that unless one knew the end of the story, one would take A for one of the most dangerous of criminals. The following are the instructions in question. They are addressed by A, Uranist, to B, Uranist, whose duty it was to force C to indulge in pederasty.

§ 1

The first time that you will have the good fortune to surprise him stealing anything you shall close the doors and tell him that you will have him imprisoned as a common thief. You shall then tell him that you have received letters from me which he has written to me and which you will have already burned beforehand and that you will give them to the police. He will be seized by a terrible fear and throw himself at your feet begging for pity. Then you shall tell him that you will not denounce him, on condition that he become your slave, without pay, and your prostitute as long as you wish it.

§ 2

If he consents you will subdue him the same evening. You shall take off his coat and tie his hands behind his back like a prisoner. You shall then remove his shoes and socks, and let him wear only his shirt and trousers.

§ 3

You shall call together all the servants who live in the house. You shall seat yourselves at the table and drink a small barrel of beer which I shall send you for that very evening and you shall smoke cigars which you will receive at the same time. When you are very comfortable, take off his suit and do with him as you will. He should wash your feet and you can ejaculate *in os* or he must kiss your buttocks if you so wish it. You may make this fellow do anything, no matter how heinous he will give himself up to all your fancies.

§ 4

During the night, place irons around his neck and feet for if he escapes you will have no more power over him.

§ 5

He will have a bunch of straw and an old quilt to lie on; no bed.

§ 6

Every evening he will wash the feet of all of you. It is very agreeable during the summer.

§ 7

If he cries give him "hell" so that he will not catch cold.

§ 8

Every morning you shall make him shave you, and for this give him 10 cents.

§ 9

He should speak only when spoken to.

§ 10

When you have to go out, or when there is no one in the house, you shall place him again in irons to make sure that he does not escape or do stupid things.

§ 11

When you beat him you will do it in the Russian manner. You will take a ladder which you will place against the wall, then you will attach him, feet on the bottom and hands above the head to the rungs of the ladder. Then take off his garment (undress him if you wish).

The body will be bound by a cord. You shall then take a knout and give him several blows on his bare buttocks. Never beat him with all your force for he is a weak youth and he will suffer atrociously where a vigorous man would feel nothing.

§ 12

Each time he does not listen to you beat him with rods.

§ 13

He must do all the work of the house.

§ 14

Now I shall describe certain pleasures which are known only in Russia and Turkey.

§ 14-a

The pleasures in question are not very common but when one possesses a fellow to whom one can do anything one should not deprive oneself of them. Here, in Russia, one must pay an enormous sum for it; but you, happy man, shall have it for nothing.

§ 14-b

Undress him and yourself. Then place yourself on his belly; he should lick your feet, chiefly between the toes and on the sole of the foot; if you want an erection, lie in such a manner that he fondle your member with one hand and your testicles with another. He should at the same time wash your feet and to put his tongue as far as possible in the anus until you have an ejaculation. This is most pleasurable.

§ 14-c

Undress him and tie his hands behind his back and also tie his feet; place him on his back, yourself on top, put your member *in os;* if you ejaculate, do not let him spit out the semen; he should swallow it whether he wants to or not. This is the Turkish procedure.

§ 15

When he has done everything you shall write to me; I shall come in person and if everything goes well I shall present you with $250. What I insist upon most is that you should ejaculate *in os* and that he should not spit out the semen. You must read my instructions every day so as not to forget anything. In these instructions you will find all you will have to do with your slave and I ask you, for your own good, to obey my instructions to the letter.

§ 16

For food you will give him plenty of milk, black bread, water, eggs, vegetables, such as cabbage, turnips, peas and potatoes. He shall have meat only on Sundays.

§ 17

He shall be free every Sunday from 10 in the morning until midday and he may go out. He may then put on his shoes and socks. Never during the week. But if he does not return on the stroke of 12 he shall be beaten with rods.

§ 18

You shall then teach him to do the following things:
1. Cultivate the garden and the fields.
2. Brush your clothes and shine your shoes.
3. Clean the stairway.
4. Sleep at night in irons (at his neck and feet).
5. Wash his master's feet.
6. He should take your member *in os*.
7. Wash your feet and buttocks.

You know that I shall keep my word, consequently, keep yours and do all I tell you to.

§ 19

You shall write me a several-page letter every other day telling me in detail what you are doing with your slave and what point you have reached in his instruction. Your slave shall carry your letter to the post office and mail it; he shall bring back your receipt. I above all desire that he know that you are writing to me so that he should be quite aware of the fact that you do all this according to my orders.

§ 20

When in the evening he serves you in the house, he should take off your clothes. In the house, he must, as a real slave, be entirely naked and at most wear his shirt. You shall re-read my instructions every night, to forget nothing. Reply immediately to tell me whether you feel yourself capable of conscientiously carrying out all my instructions to the letter. I therefore give to you my old domestic as punishment for all the tricks he has played on me. All his belongings with the exception of his trousers, shirt and slippers, belong to you; even the money you find on his person. I permit you to do all you wish with him, all that occurs to you. He has the alternatives of doing all you command him to do without pay or of being denounced to the police. For the time being, you are his only master. I shall come myself on the 21st of August. I shall expect your letters every Wednesday and Saturday.

Such are the instructions given by A to B, to force C to practice pederasty. As A had ordered him, B rented a villa where he awaited the arrival of C. C had to carry a letter from A and B had then to hold him. In fact, B received the visit of C at the villa one day, the latter carrying a letter from A. C however immediately escaped and B could not execute A's orders. But the most curious fact of the matter is that, some time after, the authorities acquainted with the case were able to establish the fact that A and C were one and the same person. A therefore wished that he himself be maltreated by B; that is to say, the convict himself gave himself up to the practice of pederasty. Was this simply a trick, as A maintained during the cross-examination, or was it a case of masochistic tendencies grafted onto a sexual perversion? A's flight, when B began seriously to carry out his orders, does not constitue a proof against the prevention of masochism for A may have not liked B's personality which he did not know before. It is also possible that despite his masochistic tendencies A may have at the last moment feared the acts he awaited. It seems to me impossible that such well thought out plans could be only a joke and if the idea of masochism is accepted this entire history should be attributed to a sort of complete irresponsibility on the part of A, who was then thirty.

Among the sexual perversions connected with the inversion of the genital senses we have just studied fetichism, sadism and masochism. We must now speak of certain perversions which exist in heterosexuals as well as in homosexuals. Just as there are heterosexuals who are attracted not by mature women but by little, immature girls, there are Uranists who seek not men but little boys. We have already said that this phenomenon was particularly widespread in ancient Greece, as a certain passage of Plato's "Banquet," among others, shows, in which Pausanias asks for a law against the love for boys. In a case published in detail by Tardieu a man attracted young boys to him and committed obscene acts upon them.

One should not believe that in all cases of sexual inversion there is a repugnance against having intercourse with young boys. There are adult Uranists who are attracted towards boys. It is very often noticed that from infancy Uranists are attracted towards their playmates. This phenomenon also exists among hetrosexuals, but is much rarer. Similar to this love of Uranists for boys we sometimes encounter women who have relations with boys. The cases of women adults having relations with very young boys are rather frequent. Tardieu has been able to gather many such observations, several of which are Devergie's and Casper's. They almost always deal with boys from five to thirteen and women from eighteen to thirty, most often domestics. A case of Casper's dealt with a mother who abused her son of nine. Tarnowsky cites the case of a man of twenty-six, psychopathologic to a great degree, who practiced pederasty with a boy of two. Against the desire for young boys may be cited those which involved a young lawyer. From the viewpoint of psychic degeneration, Tarnowsky considered his passion for old men a very bad sign. I, however, do not regard this sort of sexual inversion as a measure of the degree of psychic degeneration.

Among the other perversions exhibited by Uranists, I may also cite the excitement caused by statues. Certain Uranists go so far as to embrace the statues of men who please them. One of Krafft-Ebing's patients complained against the vine leaves which, in statues, replaced the genitals. Atheneus tells the story of a Greek who fell in love with the statue of Cupid and performed the act of sexual intercourse upon it. The violation of corpses (necrophilus) is not limited exclusively to the cadavers of the other sex. Moreover this phenomenon is, for Krafft-Ebing, of a sadistic nature. Besides, there is the well-known case published by Michea of a sergeant named Bertrand, who covered cadavers with kisses, caressed and violated them; he cut the corpse into pieces and masturbated while looking at them. Bertrand accomplishes these acts with both sexes.

There are yet other perversions which belong to the domain of sexual inversion. I know a Uranist whose companion needed only touch his genitals; he was contended with a general excitation caused by the sense of touch. He had his companion rub his body, his forehead, and the nape of the neck; this was sufficient to cause him to have an erection and subsequent ejaculation. This sexual excitation by tactile irritation is also to be observed in heterosexual relations. The inverse often takes place; that is, the excitation of a part of the body of a Uranist causes an ejaculation in the other. I have been told the case of a man who had an erection, and then ejaculated when he licked the interior of the ear of another man.

I shall here end the chapter on the phenomena of perversion observed in cases of sexual inversion. The subject is far from being exhausted; it would be necessary to write a whole book to make a complete study of it and to take into account the individuality of each patient and the peculiarities of his perversion. It would be interesting to make a comparative study of it by epochs. The books relative to the history of love are silent on this question. I believe, however, sexual perversion has in different periods varied within certain limits and I think this supposition may be based on the frequent changes of fashions.

Chapter VII

PSYCHO-SEXUAL HERMAPHRODISM

Intermediate Sex; Periodic Inversion; Playing the Woman.

We have seen that there are men who are attracted as much by men as by women. Casper had spoken before of those individuals who have relations with men as well as with women and attributed it to a kind of disgust for women which comes of abusing them. He evidently does not know those cases in which the morbid predisposition to psychic hermaphrodism existed since the beginning and manifests itself according to the circumstances in the form of a desire sometimes for men, sometimes for women. It appears moreover that hermaphrodism had already existed in antiquity, principally in ancient Greece.

Krafft-Ebing, who sought to classify the different degrees of congenital sexual inversion, has established the following forms: first, psycho-sexual hermaphrodism, in which are found traces of heterosexual tendencies with a marked predominance of homosexual tendencies. Second, homosexuality, every tendency towards the opposite sex is absent, and the sexual urge is directed only to individuals of the same sex.

138

Third, effeminacy, in which the entire psychic side of the individual deviates according to its sexual inversion. Fourth, androgyny, in which there even exists a physical transformation in connection with the sexual inversion. These divisions of Krafft-Ebing's are very practical; a very great many cases of sexual inversion may certainly be ranged in one or the other of these categories. However, classification is sometimes difficult to make—a fact which is not at all surprising. In certain forms of very acute effeminacy I have known men whose entire manner of acting recalled that of the woman, but who had intercourse only with women, and who found complete satisfaction therein. Cases of this type therefore enter groups one and three at the same time.

I would like however to enlarge upon this conception of psycho-sexual hermaphrodism. I am particularly acquainted with a series of cases in which the heterosexual urge predominates very clearly but in which the individuals are seized from time to time with homosexual desires. These individuals should be called psycho-sexual hermaphrodites, even though Krafft-Ebing supposed that in these cases the heterosexual urge is only rudimentary. I believe that by reasons of the many transitional cases one must not exclude from psychosexual hermaphrodism those cases in which the alternating desire for man and for women lasts for only a short time or extends over the entire period of life. It is easily understood that sexual inversion does not separate itself from the normal sexual life in a very sharp way. There are here to be found intermediate cases ranging from a simple trace of homosexual love to the most acute form of Uranism.

In an individual for example there may be a passing desire simply to touch the man to whom he is sympathetically inclined. This desire once satisfied immediately disappears, never to reappear. Another may experience a very keen urge for a certain man and be seized with sexual inversion each time he sees him, while apart from this he is quite normal sexually. A third is sexually excited not only by certain persons but by a whole class of men; vigorous men with blond hair, for example; when he is not in the presence of one of these men, his sexual sensations are normal. A man who has been a prey to this form of sexual inversion has described his state to me as follows: "——My disease consisted in being continually thrown from feminine to masculine sensations and vice versa. A man's body had an irresistible influence over me and greatly excited my imagination but at the same time I felt a passionate desire to embrace a woman. Even during childhood I was excited by the beauty of man and woman. From the age of seven I have been given to unbridled masturbation while thinking during the act of men. Twice I escaped from that hell; now it is no longer possible. My unhealthy imagination made me consider blond, vigorous and very healthy men as particularly desirable. This condition was very painful to me, but I could not resist it. Men's thighs and hips made me lose my head completely; likewise, a very large penis."

The man in question is today entirely cured of his homosexual desires. It is curious that dark-haired men left him indifferent and that he was excited only by a blonde head, " truly Germanic."

There are also other varieties in which sexual inversion predominates, the heterosexual desire appearing only accidentally. Sometimes, as Krafft-Ebing observes, this desire manifests itself only in dreams and plays quite a secondary role in ordinary life.

Certain Uranists presenting typical sexual inversion have short episodes in which they feel themselves drawn to a woman. I know the case of a Uranist who at a masked ball had met a young girl towards whom he felt attracted; he had sexual intercourse with her. But after the act he was seized with such disgust that he fled and he would never meet her again. In another case a Uranist was seized with a violent passion for a young girl and he believed that he could satisfy her in sexual intercourse; but because of the difference in their social standing he could never gain his end.

Cases of this kind are not very rare in the life of Uranists. Some are convinced of the uselessness of intercourse with women. When they have a passing urge for women they prefer to await patiently the return of homosexual tastes. Such is the case with an individual named X. He often practiced coition with women and found therein full and complete satisfaction; however, he does not believe that he can rid himself forever of his love for men since merely at the sight of a man towards whom he is sympathetic he feels a genital excitation. X affirms that he will no longer try to have heterosexual relations not even when he feels attracted towards women. Others seek to use these periods for intercourse with women. In certain cases, one has to admit that the homosexual impulse shows itself periodically, a fact upon which Tarnowsky particularly insists. Tarnowsky compares this state with dipsomania, for the reason that, in both cases there is a consciousness of the impossibility of all resistance. Tarnowsky likewise cites very interesting cases of individuals inflicted with periodic sexual inversion who know in advance just when they would be seized by it; the patients in question arrange matters so that everything happens in secret and escapes the knowledge of those about them.

Krafft-Ebing believes that psycho-sexual hermaphrodites are not very rare. As these men are often married and manifest indifference to their wives only momentarily, their conduct does not appear suspicious. I am personally acquainted with several of these hermaphrodites who have intercourse sometimes with their wives, sometimes with men. In a great many hermaphrodites the sex of the individual towards whom they feel sexually attracted plays, in general, no role whatever. They have a desire for a certain type and the sex of that type is for them of no importance at all. The individual's head plays the principal role in their passion, some love a blond head with short hair, others fine features, etc., no matter whether that head belongs to a man or a woman. Certain Uranists are excited only by women of a masculine aspect; by women, for example, who wear short hair.

I have remarked that a certain degree of hermaphrodism is to be encountered rather frequently before the complete development of the genitals. It is a known fact that the desire of certain boys for other boys has a decidedly sexual character and that after puberty this desire disappears. The fact that these boys often have erections when they embrace their comrades during their games proves that there is a sexual urge before puberty. This psycho-sexual hermaphrodism before puberty appears to me to be particularly frequent in cases of sexual inversion. One of my patients, a shoe fetichist, was seized with this type of fetichism in early childhood. As a child, he always wanted to kiss his instructor's and his comrades' shoes. At the same time, he conceived a passion for a little girl's shoes. After puberty this desire became heterosexual in the sense that his fetichism was directed only to women's shoes, those of wordly women, particularly.

Niemeyer lays stress on the passion of certain boys for others, such passion being analogous to love. According to him it is the awakening of the genital instinct which goes astray and misses its path. When the genital instinct is inverted the resulting inversion may manifest itself with more or less intensity. In heterosexuals certain individuals experience a more or less violent sexual urge: it is the same among homosexuals except that in the latter hyperesthesia and exaggeration of this urge appear more frequently. The aversion for either sex may also vary greatly in intensity and between simply sexual antipathy and the most intense horror may be found numerous intermediate conditions.

In a case published by Westphal there seems to be an incomplete form of sexual inversion in the sense that the man who was very effeminate and loved women's costumes was sexually attracted to women. This state may arise periodically. One of Westphal's patients who was of this type said that when he overcame his desire he was seized with excessive anguish which did not disappear until he satisfied his passion. Although he denied having intercourse with men this patient showed complete effeminacy in his ordinary life.

He played the role of women in a company of comedians and
loved to do women's work.

Westphal rightly stresses the difficulty in understanding
these patients. Men often dress themselves as women to be
able to commit thefts more easily and to put the police on the
wrong track. This point had to be taken into consideration
in the case cited by Westphal for his patient had previously
committed a series of robberies. However Westphal was
convinced that his patient had a morbid desire to dress as a
woman.

Chapter XIII

ETIOLOGY

Onanism as a Cause of Inversion; Heredity as a Cause; Neurotic Disorders; Accidental Causes; Mutual Masturbation as a Cause; Separation of Sex as a Cause; Abuse of Coition as a Cause; Physical Hermaphrodism; Senile Pederasty.

The causes of sexual inversion are numerous and differ according to the author. Caspar divided his patients into two groups, one in which the desire for the same sex was congenital and the other in which it was acquired because of the abuse of coition with women which produced a sort of disgust. We shall see further on that these ideas of Caspar's are still endorsed entirely or in part by a great many authors. Besides Caspar's two groups Gley supposes a third in which sexual inversion is due to the fact that the act done at first through unwholesome curiosity later becomes a habit. Tarnowsky accepts in general Casper's divisions but at the same time includes in the second group those cases of sexual inversion that are due to bad education, to bad example, or to certain mental maladies. Mantegazza does not dwell much on the etiology of sexual inversion in his anthropological and historic studies of sexual intercourse among men. He claims that the origin of all sexual perversions may be attributed to two causes: the difficulty of practicing coition normally and

144

the desire to procure a new pleasure. Krafft-Ebing also distinguishes between acquired and congenital sexual inversion. He believes that certain causes (which we shall enumerate later) particularly sexual abuse and onanism may later cause sexual inversion in a normal individual. These causes may operate most effectively during the developing period of the genital organs; an opinion which is shared by Tarnowsky. Contrary to acquired sexual inversion congenital inversion is tainted from the beginning with perversion without the previous existence of a desire for women.

However, most of the cases of sexual inversion which are considered as acquired do not seem very convincing to me. It is hardly possible to enter into general considerations to maintain that in most cases sexual inversion already existed in a latent state during childhood. Krafft-Ebing's conscientious classification includes very few cases of acquired perversion and I am convinced that even the latter are not entirely beyond objection in the sense that sexual perversion therein rather precedes the heterosexual urge.

Thus, Observation 72 made by that author does not at all prove the existence of acquired sexual inversion nor its differentiation from psychic hermaphrodism. The patient in question whom Krafft-Ebing considers a victim of acquired sexual inversion practiced mutual masturbation with a friend at the age of twelve before going with women. During masturbation, which he practiced for a long time, he fancied himself a dancer who was having intercourse with an officer. When the patient did not masturbate for a long time he desired intercourse with women; but this fact rather favors psycho-sexual hermaphrodism even though the patient's erotic dreams were always about women. This patient's singular ideas during masturbation preceded heterosexual desires and these ideas were very clearly of a homosexual character.

Another observation of Krafft-Ebing's, Number 73, is also not entirely beyond objection for there are very clear signs of psycho-sexual hermaphrodism in the history of this patient. There was in particular a period in his life during which he was equally attracted by both men and women with the peculiarity that his sexual desires were directed towards immature individuals. Later this man manifested sexual inversion exclusively which perhaps was not yet quite clear in that women did not fill him with horror and that his aversion for the feminine sex was not absolute. This patient on the whole was most likely a psychic hermaphrodite. The difference is fully explained by the fact that Krafft-Ebing's definition of psycho-sexual hermaphrodism is more restricted than mine and that is why these different cases are cases of sexual inversion for him.

Another observation of Krafft-Ebing's (Observation 74) gives a clearer example of acquired sexual inversion. The patient in question, whose sexual desires were very strong, first sought to satisfy them in brothels. Later he noticed that although the sight of a nude woman excited him very much he had neither orgasm nor ejaculation even when the woman tried to provoke him through masturbation. As the patient kept on experiencing sexual excitement even on leaving the brothel, the fact may be explained only as a case of normal sexual instinct with neurasthenic impotence caused by masturbation.

It appears to me, however in quite a general way that an insufficient voluptuous sensations during the sexual act should be attributed to sexual inversion in a great many cases. I particularly know men who, with a vague desire for women, had no voluptuous sensations during coition, despite erection and ejaculation. On the other hand, these sensations are most intense when they practice a sexual act with a man for whom they have a psycho-sexually hermaphroditic urge.

I therefore think that after all these considerations a great many cases of acquired sexual inversion should be considered to be the result of psycho-sexual hermaphrodism. I do not deny that one may from time to time meet with cases of sexual inversion in which homosexual desires and tendencies crop up after the existence of normal desire for women. But at the same time I believe that we are dealing here essentially with a clinical division and that pure cases of acquired sexual inversion are rare. Almost all research workers are in accord on this point. I find that on the whole there are few authors who consider acquired sexual inversion as an habitual phenomenon.

To avoid all confusion let us repeat that one must consider as acquired those cases in which the desire for man is preceded by that for woman. Properly speaking all cases of sexual inversion ought to be considered as acquired since under certain conditions there is no reason, when they manifest themselves from the age of eight, to consider them congenital rather than acquired. In the same sense acquired sexual perversion is extremely rare. I find that only those authors who have made very few observations consider congenital perversion as very infrequent. An eminent criminologist who is very much occupied in the study of this question has told me that so far as he is concerned perversion in the case of most pederasts and Uranists dates from childhood and that it arises from a sort of congenital predisposition.

Even admitting that from time to time they meet with cases which are very clearly those of acquired sexual inversion, almost all authors are in accord in saying that the etiological causes are the same for congenital inversion as for acquired inversion. We may characterize them as neuroses or psychoses due to overtension of the central nervous system. Morel, who had introduced the word "degeneration," supposes that degeneration takes on more serious forms in the offspring than in the parents. Consequently when there is a light form of degeneration of the central nervous system in the parents, hysteria for example, serious psychic trouble may be found in the children.

It is certain that in all cases of sexual inversion whether acquired or congenital, where perversion is involved, we find a very burdened heredity. Krafft-Ebing, Ratou, Charcot, Maguan, Blumstock, Kowolewsky, Bourneville, Raoult, Gley, Tarnowsky and a great many other authors are all in accord on this point. Only Westphal does not commit himself on the question whether or not there is involved a neuro- or psychopathic state provoked by a greatly overburdened nervous heredity. The distinction is interesting from a clinical standpoint, but etiologically, it plays a secondary role; since we know that degeneration takes place in purely nervous maladies as well as in psychic affections and that both are connected with nervous heredity.

In studying the question of the degeneration of the nervous system, it is necessary also to place besides well-known nervous and mental maladies a certain number of other causes involved in nervous heredity. Of such are alcoholism and consanguinary marriages. In the case described by Magnan and Charcot, the etiological element consists of the great difference between the ages of the father and mother, the difference being thirty-one years. Nervous heredity may in certain cases manifest itself only in the form of eccentricities, religious exaltation, etc. I know several cases of consanguinary marriages in which the father of a Uranist child was a liver in the full sense of the word, celebrated for his successes with women. Krafft-Ebing says he knows cases in which sexual inversion existed to a very feeble degree among the ancestors. Among the causes of psychic defect, Tarnowsky includes syphilis. He cites many cases to uphold his opinion; but his observations appear to me not convincing enough to establish the etiological role of syphilis if one takes into consideration the extent of this affection. The great importance which Tarnowsky attributes from the standpoint of nervous heredity to serious ailments in the parents during a short while before conception, such as typhoid fever, pneumonia, anemia, chronic fatigue, etc., does not appear to me to be true and has no connection with sexual inversion.

Atavism plays a unique role in nervous heredity. One may find the father and mother in very good health but in pushing the investigation further discovers a nervous or psychic affection in the grandparents.

Krafft-Ebing also cites other facts to uphold his theory of neuro- or psychopathic heredity: first, the fact of the precocious appearance of sexual life in sexual inverts; second, the exaggerated character that this malady assumes on the psychic side of love; third, the very great frequency of neuroses, hysteria, neurasthenia, etc., in certain cases, beside a little developed intelligence, a remarkable talent for music, poetry, etc. Finally, the disorders of psychic equilibrium are in certain cases sufficiently remote to be transformed into passing or chronic mental disturbances. Other nervous or psychic troubles could in most cases be ascertained. Several of the Roman emperors, being victims of sexual inversion, were degenerates inflicted with psychic affections. In a case cited by Westphal there existed recurrent insanity, in another idiocy. In Gock's case and in several others there are states of melancholia. I have discovered myself in a case ideas of persecution. I shall return further on to cases of sexual inversion complicated by the presence of epilepsy, progressive paralysis and dementia.

It is evident that psycho- or neuropathic heredity does not exhaust the question of the etiology of sexual perversion. There still exist a great many difficult points to explain. One may ask for example why all degenerates are not tainted with sexual inversion. One must admit as an explanation that in degenerates inflicted with sexual inversion the sexual instinct presents the *locus minoris resistentiae*. Just as in degenerates heredity manifests itself for one in the form of the idea of persecution, for another in the form of epilepsy, degeneration, in Uranists takes the form of sexual inversion. We do not know why epilepsy is found in the one, and sexual inversion in the other; no more than we know why of two persons catching cold one has only catarrh while the other has articular rheumatism.

It is therefore certain, as we have seen, that a great many Uranists are the progeny of families possessing a neuropathic heredity. But it is very difficult to obtain precise data on this point for it often happens that neuropathic heredity exists in numerous cases in which one cannot discover it. When these patients are questioned as to the alcoholism or the mental

maladies of their parents their replies are not always satisfying for they try to keep them secret when they know them.
However, I must say that it is difficult to prove the existence
of a neuropathic heredity in all cases of sexual inversion in
men.   One must also deal with the present tendency of certain authors who considerably enlarge the domain of nervous
heredity and who thus discover it in almost all cases of
phychic or mental affections.

We have said that the predisposition to sexual inversion is
almost always congenital.   However one must admit the existence of occasional causes which favor the beginning of
sexual perversion as in acquired inversion.   Even in cases in
which sexual inversion may be observed from childhood we
can find only a morbid predisposition, making it impossible
to deny that the beginning of this perversion is sometimes
provoked by an extraneous cause.   In a child this may be the
purely accidental touching of his genitals by a man.   The
morbid affection is then developed by a fatal association between the remembrance of the contact and the mental image
of the man.   It is therefore impossible to differentiate clearly
between congenital cases, properly so-called, and those in
which sexual perversion appears through an accidental cause.

Hammond reports the history of an individual tainted with
sexual inversion in the form of pederasty, a passion to which
he became addicted when as a child he saw two dogs copu-
lating.   The young boy thought that this was done in the
anus.   To imitate this act, he introduced a pencil into his rectum and felt a pain and then a very agreeable sensation.

Ought we to say that in the boy who later became a passive
pederast sexual perversion manifested itself through what he
saw?   We do not think so, for how are we to explain the
voluptuous sensation he experienced on introducing the pencil
into his rectum and which led him to repeat the same experi-
ment.   Another occasional cause whatsoever would certainly
have been sufficient to provoke sexual inversion and the tendency to passive pederasty in this individual who has never
felt an urge for women.   A normal child or a normal man

could introduce a pencil into his rectum every day without causing sexual perversion.

I do not wish to say, however, that occasional causes have in themselves no importance whatsoever. It is thus probable that in cases of psycho-sexual hermaphrodism, an occasional cause may determine the direction taken by the sexual life of an individual, at least, for a certain time. But we must suppose that in all cases, sexual inversion exists latently in the individual and is awakened only in encountering a sympathetic man. One must note the moment when the individual commences to be conscious of his sexual inversion, for that moment the inversion begins.

If we assume that occasional causes may favor the cropping out of sexual perversion we can hardly hope to stop the growth of a morbid predisposition by prophylactic measures. It is in fact certain that sexual inversion cannot be systematically caused by bad habits. Even admitting that bad examples and unwholesome curiosity can play a certain role in this question, it is difficult to believe, with Tarnowsky, that we can by a well conceived prophylaxis impede in a great number of cases the development of sexual inversion in predisposed individuals. Nevertheless, we must try, as much as we can, to overcome the development of this sexual inversion. We shall return to this point in discussing its treatment.

It appears very probable that in the case of a predisposition to sexual inversion the occasional causes may play a definite role determining the manner in which the genital instinct will be satisfied. But, on the other hand, we must say that here also there is a predisposition for certain sexual acts, for passive pederasty, for example. Otherwise, I could not see why there should be individuals who from the beginning are satisfied only with passive pederasty.

If we admit the role of accidental causes, we must not confuse those which lead to the realization of an act of perversion with those which cause the beginning of the urge for the perversion. When a man who has been a prey of sexual inversion for a long time finds the occasion to satisfy his

passion with another man, one should not consider this encounter as the occasional cause which led to the beginning of
the desire. That is an error which is committed frequently.

The following is an example which well shows what one
must understand to be an occasional cause, in a predisposed
individual. It deals with an individual who until the time of
the incident in question was absolutely normal sexually, in
that he had had intercourse only with women. In Paris, he
made the acquaintance of a person who asked him to accompany her home. He accepted this proposition, very much excited, wishing to pass the night with her. The young person
undressed and the man discovered with stupefaction that the
one he had followed was a man dressed as a woman. Under
normal conditions merely the idea of intercourse with a man
would have been sufficient to reject all physical contact. But
here he did nothing of the kind; he let himself be masturbated
by the other, and he became from that moment the clearest
case of sexual inversion.

I would like to make a study in what follows of a series of
occasional causes which, under certain conditions, favor the
appearance of sexual perversion. However, I do not consider
most of these facts proved; for we have not a sufficient number of observations for establishing the real and indisputable
value of these causes. It seems that each author contents
himself with quoting the observations of others without adding anything of his own.

Moral contagion and bad example are of prime importance.
Tarnowsky emphasizes this, being of the opinion that a boy
inflicted with sexual inversion and raised in a boarding school
could spread the disease all about him. He claims that the
young man accomplishes the act by first thinking of a woman.
But when he has for a sufficient length of time practiced pederasty in this way, i.e., in always thinking of a woman, his
entire sexual life gradually becomes wrongly orientated;
through habit, he becomes a Uranist and finds his satisfaction
in pederasty exclusively.

One can win over only those who allow themselves to be

won over. The sexual act depends on the voluptuous sensations provoked by it; it is evident that the act in question will be accomplished only by those who experience voluptuous sensations therein. Some young boys are well-disposed to mutual masturbation, but as soon as they experience women, intercourse with men becomes impossible for them. I know several cases in which mutual masturbation practiced during childhood had never caused sexual inversion.

Tarnowsky is of the opinion that the desire to imitate a certain person, unwholesome curiosity and the search for new pleasures may force individuals of weak character to practice abnormal acts, and to habituate themselves thereto without their possessing an innate desire for them.

Coffignon attributes the great spread of pederasty during recent times to the more intimate relations which have been established between Europe on one side and Asia and Africa on the other: according to him, this fact may be particularly true of England. He also believes, without showing proof for his assertion, that Uranism has for several years become widespread in Germany. If it is true that pederasty is developed by bad example and one cannot deny that literature plays a certain etiologic role in its propogation.

Tarnowsky shares Coffignon's opinion that, in the propogation of pederasty, mutual masturbation in boarding schools and in prisons plays a very considerable role. One may assume theoretically that the repetition of the excitation produced by mutual masturbation may lead to sexual inversion, only the observations pertaining thereto are still few, so that it is actually impossible to decide the question one way or the other. When we discover sexual inversion in an individual who had previously practiced mutual masturbation with a boy, one must not lightly conclude that masturbation caused the sexual inversion in this individual. Most often the inversion existed previously in him. Although mutual masturbation is quite widespread in certain places one must not conclude that a Uranist is produced by it, there is not sufficient reason to regard masturbation and Uranism as cause and effect. I have seen an epidemic of this type in full vigor in a school in Berlin where mutual masturbation had been introduced and practiced shamelessly by a student who is today a well-known actor. Although I know the names of a great many Uranists in Berlin, none of them are old pupils of this school. On the other hand, I know many pupils of this same school who today are absolutely normal sexually.

Chevalier, Krauss, Appert, Tarnowsky and others consider privation from sexual intercourse with women as one of the causes of sexual inversion. Sexual inversion may be seen where men long deprived of women get together. This form may have according to Chevalier and Ulrichs only a passing character and disappears to make way for the normal sexual instinct when the external conditions are modified. Chevalier speaks of the army, navy, prisons, boarding schools, hospitals, in this connection. Tarnowsky, who attributes great importance to moral contagion, must admit that a great many circumstances ordinarily comes into play to cause the extended practice of pederasty in boarding schools, etc.

Perhaps one must attribute a certain influence on the subsequent development of sexual inversion to the rigorous separation of the sexes among children. Certain authors are decidedly of the opinion that the rigorous separation of the sexes during puberty causes young boys to be sexually attracted to men.

However, I could not resolve this problem definitely. If we want to have a clear and precise solution of it we must be able to prove that the individuals tainted with sexual inversion have been quite rigorously separated from the other sex during puberty and I have never been able to make this observation. To elucidate this same question we must prove, on the other hand, that the boys who have not been separated from girls during puberty have not become Uranists or are less subject to sexual inversion than boys raised under opposite conditions. It would be interesting to determine whether sexual inversion in America where relations between boys and girls are freer is less widespread than in other countries.

In fact, according to H. T. Fink, the separation of the sexes
in America is much rarer than among us who put off as
much as possible the time when young men may enter the
society of women.

In America there is little separation of the sexes that, according to Fink, each little girl in the schools has her "beau,"
a boy of fourteen to seventeen, without any disagreeable consequences. It would therefore be very interesting to determine whether sexual inversion is less frequent in America
than elsewhere.

Moralists who preach the rigorous and most possibly prolonged separation of the sexes during childhood and youth
ought to ask themselves whether they would not be favoring
sexual inversion thereby. A gentleman whom I know, who
is a psycho-sexual hermaphrodite, attributes his sexual perversion exclusively to the education he received. He told me
that the genital instinct was developed in him at a very early
age; but as he was entirely deprived of the society of women
his desires were directed towards men; later women could
excite him from time to time but his desire for men did not
diminish.

Meier also mentions the rigorous separation of the sexes
as one of the causes which contributed to development of
pederasty in Greece. Most often women lived in retirement
from men. Besides it was impossible because of the education which women received during that epoch for men to
find complete satisfaction and moral aid in their wives, while
today almost the opposite is true. It is for all these reasons
that men turned to boys to whom, moreover, they were attracted by quite a spiritual bond. This rigorous separation
of the sexes is also considered as a cause of the frequency of
pederasty among the Mohammedans.

Chavalier and a great many other authorities cite the fear
of a contagious disease in intercourse with women and the
fear of pregnancy as among causes of sexual inversion. Fear
of impotence in sexual intercourse with women may enter
the same class of facts. I find however that the facts upon

which these considerations are based are insufficient. There are in particular certain observations which pass from one book to another without being checked. Chevalier reports a case cited by E. Hoffman wherein a criminal pederast had evaded normal intercourse because he feared to see the woman become pregnant while such danger did not exist in intercourse with boys. One should not however place too much credence in what an accused person states. I do not wish to deny that the causes of which we have just spoken can sometimes play an etiological role; but such causes are not frequent, for it appears to me impossible that a man unless he is forced by morbid sexual tendencies could find satisfaction in relations with another man.

The frequence of pederasty among the Catholic clergy is attributed by some to celibacy and the fear of the consequences possible in relations with women. I believe that the fact is to be construed in another way. The inclination for a calling which includes celibacy is rather noticeable among the persons in whom the desire for women is from the beginning quite undeveloped.

Tarnowsky declares that sexual inversion may be developed in individuals who make a profession of it. To gain their livelihood sometimes normal men give themselves to sexual inverts, and later are themselves inflicted with the malady; in other words, sexual inversion is in this case artificial. However, no author attempts to define the limit precisely between the performance of an unnatural act and the perversion itself of the sexual instinct. It seems doubtful to me that merely the practice can cause sexual inversion in normal individuals.

I must completely reject the opinion of Moreau that masturbation may be the cause of the sexual inversion. It is an absolutely false conception which confounds the cause with the effect. A great many Uranists masturbate because they cannot otherwise satisfy their genital instinct.

If I do not consider masturbation the cause of Uranism, I nevertheless admit that under certain conditions it may favor

the development of sexual inversion. The fact that at the beginning of his sexual evolution the Uranist thinks only of
men while masturbating, aggravates the sexual inversion in
the sense that his sexual desires associate themselves more
and more with the idea of men. It also happens that masturbation practiced under these conditions strengthens his
impotence towards women and turns the individual more and
more towards men. Krafft-Ebing and L. Casper insist on the
unwholesome influence of masturbation on individuals inflicted with sexual inversion or presenting a morbid predisposition to this malady. They consider that masturbation destroy
the esthetic, ideal and normal desire that men experience for
women.

Certain authors attribute the same etiological role to a life
of debauch and to the abuse of normal coition that they do
to masturbation. Coffignon says that these causes intervene
in the development of sexual inversion, principally among the
leisure classes. I do not believe this to be true and I am of
the opinion that debauchees to find new pleasures do not
practice pederasty as often as they are said to do.

Even from a theoretic point of view, I cannot find a connection between excessive coition with women and the development of the desire for men. How can a man who feels
sexual aversion for men find himself one day attracted to
them for the sole reason that he has abused women? It is just
as impossible as to see an individual satiated with pastry and
cake seized one day with a passion for the dirt and filth that is
thrown into the street.

If the abuse of women really leads to pederasty it should
be admitted by the same reason that homosexual love long
practiced ought to lead through disgust to women. Unfortunately it is not so. I do not know of a single case of this
kind.

Stark includes among the causes of pederasty a diminution
in the intensity of the volptuous sensation felt in coition; in
that the contraction of the sphincter of the vulva becomes
insufficient to cause the complete sensation; the man there-

fore seeking the more vigorous contraction of the anal sphincter. Mantegazza also considers the cause of pederasty the desire experienced by some to feel their member enclosed to the greatest degree, which makes them prefer the small anus to the larger vagina. If that were so this desire would explain to us at the same time the *immissio in anum femina*. It is inexplicable how this practice could give way to a pederasty of men or of boys.

According to Stark, one should also take into account the "elevated taste" for the anus. Perhaps, if certain individuals indeed seek this sort of satisfaction, does it not deal with sexual inversion as well as with a special type of perversion recalling cophrophagy?

Tarnowsky is also of the opinion that certain individuals inflicted with hyperesthesia of the genital senses may be led to practice active pederasty. When these individuals cannot practice normal coition they masturbate or seek a passive pederast. I believe this author goes a little too far, for one should assume the existence, in a great many of these individuals not only of the hyperesthesia of the genital sense but also of a sexual perversion if indeed these individuals can practice pederasty during excessive genital excitement. Of course, I do not deny that the fact could be produced without the presence of perversion; but in this case, there is no question of perversion in the sense employed by Krafft-Ebing or by me; but of perversity when the genital senses are excited to such a point, many things may happen. In a trial which took place in a small city of Southern Germany, the accused said that he had practiced sodomy with a sheep because when he was very excited he had no other means of satisfaction.

Gley lays special stress on the influence exerted by certain enjoyments. He believes that men ceaselessly seek new excitations for sexual satisfaction. Through habit an abnormal state develops that of sexual inversion, particularly when the new excitement sought by the individual is found in sexual intercourse with men. Tarnowsky also supposes very plausibly that the more young people have intercourse with boys the more easily sexual inversion develops. Let one compare this fact with the opinion that the abuse of women may lead to sexual inversion. It is the entire absence of the critical spirit which has had the most contradictory causes attributed to the inversion. I believe I ought to say here once again that I do not deny the possibility of this fact, but that we lack material which would permit us to establish it definitely.

I have just cited certain etiological causes which may apparently lead to sexual inversion. I have already said that without denying their role, we should not, however, attribute too great importance to them. If a distinction had been established between perversity and perversion, a distinction already indicated by Krafft-Ebing, a great many errors would have been avoided. What for certain writers proves to be the state of perversion, constitutes in reality only an act of perversity.

In fine, let us say, to complete our discussion that there is no relation between physical hermaphrodism and sexual inversion. Gley however claims such a relationship and forms a special group in which sexual inversion is produced by physical hermaphrodism. To uphold this opinion, he cites a remarkable case published by Magitot. It deals with an individual who on being examined was found to be a man but whose genital organs resembled a woman's to so great an extent that when he was born he was declared to be a female. This individual subsequently married a man and had sexual intercourse with him but at the same time he had relations with women. It was this case that Gley used to establish the group in question. However, I believe that before establishing a new etiological group it would be necessary to study in detail the psychic side of the sexual life of the individuals placed in that category in order to determine beyond a doubt whether they have a strong desire for men, or merely an indifference.

It is the same with a case recorded by Tourtuil dealing with physical hermaphrodism. A person was legally married to a man. The husband often practiced coition with this person without ever finding satisfaction therein. After having consulted a great many people he decided to submit his wife to an official examination to prove that she was an hermaphrodite with predominance of the masculine sex. The husband could easily introduce his member but not deeply enough. The marriage was finally annulled. It is curious to note that the hermaphrodite here claimed to feel a desire for men. One must therefore admit that in this hermaphroditic man there at the same time existed a sexual inversion in the form of homosexual tendencies. However after attentively reviewing this case I came to the conclusion that this hermaphrodite really had no desire for men but that he pretended to, hoping in this way to impede the annulment of his marriage that assured him his social position.

I therefore entirely share the opinion of Krafft-Ebing that there is no relation whatever between physical hermaphrodism and Uranism. Tardieu had already observed that in physical hermaphrodism the psychic and moral faculties and the sphere of sensations are not influenced by the malformation of the sexual organs.

There is a series of maladies in which sexual inversion is frequently to be met with. Epilepsy heads this list. According to Tarnowsky sexual perversion is frequent in epilepsy, and that writer forms a special morbid group based on the relation between epilepsy and sexual perversion. Tarnowsky believes that in some patients the appearance of sexual inversion ought to be considered as the same as epilepsy, and that in this sense, one may speak of epileptic pederasty. He cites as proof the case of a man who had had intercourse only with women and who had never presented any sign of sexual perversion; one day, in an epileptic fit and under the influence of liquor he violated a boy of fourteen. He remembered nothing, and later no one ever observed any further trace of sexual perversion in him. Senile pederasty, thus named by Tarnowsky, may often be discovered in cases of senile dementia; the aberration of the genital instinct may be the predominant symptom. This form often begins, according to Tarnowsky, with the use of vulgar expressions in conversations about sexual intercourse; especially when the conversation is with a boy. These old men ordinarily teach the boys the passive role in pederasty, but some time they prefer to play the passive role, and therefore have the boys take the active part. Senile pederasty may even force the patient to violation. In senile dementia there may also be observed sadistic tendencies complicated by sexual inversion. The pain inflicted on boys excite the patient's sexual instincts.

Sexual inversion may sometimes appear in general paralysis at the initial stages. According to Tarnowsky, it should be suspected when the individual openly speaks of his sexual life, hiding nothing thereof. He claims that these individuals take no precautions whatever to hide their inversion—a fact which should indicate a psychic disturbance.

Chevalier also supposes the existence of paralytic pederasty in the beginnings of general paralysis, in senile dementia, and in certain other cerebral disorders in which sexual inversion appears temporarily only. In these cases a real impulsion exists which the patient cannot resist.

From a purely historic viewpoint I believe I ought to cite a series of causes to which Meier attributes the development of pederasty in Greece. He believes that the tendency of the ancient Greeks to form cliques favored the development of Uranistic love; this opinion is shared by a great many writers. In the countries where these male groups were viewed with suspicion pederasty did not become so popular as in other states. Pederasty, Meier believes, may have been less frequent in Athens than elsewhere, attributing the fact to the power the tyrants exercised in that city; they sought particularly to fight these groups which they feared.

Stress is laid also upon the etiological role played by gymnastics which gave young people vigor and beauty whose attraction was greater than that of the weak and ill-developed boys in those countries in which gymnastics were not indulged in. Certain writers, Cicero and Plutarch among others, state that in the gymnasiums men were in intimate contact with each other and that this intimacy was not without its influence on pederasty. In Doric Greece and in Sparta pederasty was favored by the particular constitutions of these states. Children at the age of seven were transferred from their parents to the State. They were governed by a male adult who was not only their friend and companion but also their instructor. This deprivation of family care and this intimacy with a strange adult man may have also favored the development of pederasty.

Meier finally cites the love of study which in young people may have favored pederasty in a nobler form. The boys felt themselves attracted to their master and as the latter was not paid there was established between them an intimacy often elevated character which does not at all resemble that which exists today between teacher and pupil.

Chapter IX

REVIEW OF THEORIES

Plato and Mantegazza; Sex and Smell; Heredity and Inversion; Schopenhauer's Theory; Moll's Theory.

To complete the preceding chapter, and to throw a new light on the question of etiology, let us here recall several theories propounded by certain observers apropos of sexual inversion. In Plato's "Banquet," Aristophanes jestingly explains sexual inversion by the following myth: In the beginning there were on earth three sexes: the masculine, the feminine and a third known as androgyne. At that time men and women were not formed as they are today: they each had four legs, two faces, two sets of genitals, etc. When these men revolted against the gods, Jupiter decided to make them weaker, and to this end, divided each individual in two equal parts: one man became two men, one woman two women and each androgyne a man and a woman. But then each part began to search for its counterpart. The men who had before been part of an androgyne sought other feminine counterparts; from whence rose love for women. On the other hand those men who were part of the older complete man sought to unite themselves to men; from whence springs love among men. In this way Aristophanes pretended to explain sexual inversion.

Parmenides, celebrated philosopher of antiquity, may also have tried, according to Virey, to explain Uranistic love in his book *Preri Guseos.*

According to him a normal body is born when the sperm of the parents mix intimately during the sexual act. When the liquids do not mix intimately, beings are born who later seek what they lack; that is to say, persons of the same sex; and that is why effeminate men seek men, etc. (Virey).

I give here the explanation communicated to me by a Uranist. According to him the origin of sexual inversion may be due to the influence of the mother during pregnancy on the foetus. If during pregnancy the mother is very excited and passionately desires her husband when the genitalia of the foetus are being formed the boy, on being born, conserves this desire for man. One of Krafft-Ebing's patients has given a similar explanation: He claims his father had wished a girl to be born and that because of this wish the masculine foetus got the ideas of a girl and later became the prey of sexual inversion.

There has been much insistence on the role played by the impressions of pregnant mothers upon the character of their children. The observed facts are rather numerous and are to be found in a number of works. Liebault cites the following facts: Victor Hugo is imputed to have said that he owed his poetic talent to his mother because during her pregnancy she had made long journeys to exceptionally beautiful countries. Marie Stauart's son could not see an unsheathed sword without feeling ill; this is said to be due to the fact that Rizzio the Queen's lover was stabbed in the presence of Marie Stuart while she was pregnant. Ramdohr has also tried to explain homosexual tendencies. But his explanations are very awkward with nothing that is salient or original. Mantegazza has propounded a very singular theory. He claims that the perversion of the genital instinct is produced by an anomaly in the anatomic arrangement of the nerves. Thus, in passive pederasts the nerves normally going

to the genital organs terminate in the rectal and anal mucuous
membrances, and consequently voluptuous sensations may be
produced in them only by the excitation of the rectum. This
theory was justly opposed by Krafft-Ebing. It explains only
passive pederasty which is far rarer than active pederasty;
then the explanation which it gives of passive pederasty itself
is of little value.

In fact, what excites the passive pederast is the *membrum
virile; immissio in rectum* gives him sexual satisfaction. Masturbation satisfies him only when he is thinking of a man.
This representation is the *sine qua non* of his enjoyment and
Mantegazza neglects it completely. Besides, if the friction
exercised in the rectum causes an orgasm, it is useless to seek
the explanation of this phenomenon in an anomaly of the
nerve paths. There are men who have voluptuous sensations
by other excitations of the nerves; contact with the back,
feet, forehead. Ought we to say that in such cases the nerves
of the penis terminate in the forehead, etc.? The seat of the
voluptuous sensations, if we are dealing here with a general
sensation, is located in the member of the passive pederast;
only it seems that the sexual act can begin only by way of
the reflex part of the rectum.

Since we recognize the theory which attributes sexual inversion to an anomaly of the peripheric nerves as insufficient,
we are obliged to seek for an explanation of the aberration of
the genital senses in the psychic processes. As the genital
organs properly so-called function normally in these cases,
we cannot look for the seat of the disease in them. It is the
action of the psyche on the genital senses which in the inversion of the genital instinct is not normal. All the mental
images that awaken the genital instinct excite the genital
organs. The genital senses of man are in a normal state excited by the image of a woman; in the Uranist the excitation
is caused by the idea of a man. In him, the influence of ideas
on the sexual urge are consequently misdirected. We are thus
led to place the seat of sexual inversion in that place where
the ideas awaken the sexual instinct. That is to say according

to modern notions of psychology in the central nervous system or more particularly in the brain. The fact remains the same since the idea which awakens the sexual instinct has its origin in the momentary perception of the senses, or comes from a mental presentation, a play of the imagination. In both cases the process has its point of departure in the brain more particularly in the cerebral surface, where conscious states are involved.

Two French authors, Magnan and Gley, have gone rather far in speaking of a feminine brain in Uranists. They claim that the brain of these patients, provided with all the attributes of the masculine sex, present essentially feminine characteristics. Krafft-Ebing rejected this theory after an autopsy of a Uranist. Other autopsies on Uranists made by Recklinghausen have shown nothing in the brain which could explain sexual inversion in the patients. I do not believe that the question relative to the feminine character of the brain of Uranists can be definitely decided.

If we admit that the cause of sexual inversion is to be found in the brain without its presenting any signs of effeminacy we have to locate the seat of the malady more precisely, more closely. This question is particularly important when the modification bears exclusively on the genital instinct and leaves the other phenomena intact. I raise this point because numerous errors are committed in reference to the theory of cerebral localizations, and because we already possess some ideas about the localization of the genital instinct.

We know nothing precise about the anatomic seat of sexual inversion. We may however suppose that there are ganglionary cells in the cerebral surface, which plays a considerable role in sexual sensations, although no one can say precisely where they are. Krafft-Ebing believes that the genital sphere is found situated in the cerebral surface, near the olfactory sphere. According to Ferrier, the olfactory center is located in the gyrus uncinatus, according to Zuckerkaude in the horn of Ammon; Krafft-Ebing upholds this localization, basing it on the close relation which exists between the olfactory sense and the genital sense, which no one can deny.

Krafft-Ebing cites, to uphold the hypothesis, a work by Althaus which insists on the close relation which exists between the olfactory sense and the genital sense in animals. The learned Viennese professor also reports a great many examples confirming the existence of the same relationship in man. He cites in this connection the exciting influence of certain flowers; then several cases of violent love in men who have discerned a particular odor in women, as in the case of Henry IV, King of France, among others. It is also said that Henry III, King of France, was seized with a violent passion for Marie de Cleves, as the result of wiping himself one day with that lady's chemise, soaked in her perspiration. We have already seen that Henry III was rightfully considered a Uranist. Even though this story of Marie de Cleves be true, it does not at all invalidate the fact of this King's Uranistic tendencies, since we know that homosexuals may be seized with a momentary passion for women. I doubt these stories. The connection between the appearance of a violent passion and the fact of wiping oneself with a chemise covered with perspiration could very well have been invented later. It is sufficient to consider the fantasy with which men interweave their tales of love to understand how easy it is to make mistakes, especially when it has to do with an extraordinary phenomenon like Henry III's passion, for example. I may not be far from the truth in believing that this history was fabricated in its entirety to hide Henry III's Uranistic tendency as much as possible.

However, I do not believe that this theory is true. First, we have not the right to conclude the anatomic neighborhood of two centers from their functional relationship; then, although it is impossible to deny the connection between the perception of certain odors and the excitation of the genital senses, one must not forget that there are a great many odors which have no influence at all over them, leading to the supposition that it is only the centers of certain olfactory perceptions that are to be found beside the genital centers. In the third place, the relationship between the olfactory perception and the sexual instinct is no nearer than that between the sexual instinct and other external perceptions such as the tactile and auditory perceptions, etc. The sight of a pretty woman may excite us as much as the odor of her body; the contact of her breasts is certainly more exciting than the odor emanating from her skin. In a word, we may be thus led to suppose the nearness of the genital center to the visual or tactile center. Now, this conclusion appears to me wrong for the reasons I have just given. Finally, one may ask whether there really is an autonomous center for sexual perceptions or whether the latter are found as numerous zones scattered over the entire surface of the cerebral surface.

A very singular theory is that of Jaeger. It corresponds in all points with the idea of the author in the importance of the olfactory sense: for the Uranist the entire body of a woman, the breasts and torso in particular, give forth a repugnant odor which makes it impossible for him to find in her the satisfaction of his genital senses. On the other hand the psychic elements of homosexuals are in harmony with those of other men. This theory of Jaeger's is founded on the very real fact that the odor of women contain's something repugnant to the Uranist. Jaeger merely forgot to prove that the sexual urge is provoked by the olfactory sense alone. Now, we have already seen that the genital senses likewise have a connection with the other senses, with those of sight and of hearing, for example.

Krafft-Ebing has tried to explain sexual inversion from etiological facts. He supposes that congenital sexual inversion is transmitted by way of heredity. The rigorous distinction which he establishes between acquired sexual inversion and congenital inversion does not appear to me to be indispensable to the confirmation of the theory. I think that the morbid desire for individuals of the same sex acquired by an ancestor is transmitted to the progeny. Sexual inversion has been encountered in virile individuals. Krafft-Ebing's theory is worthy of being taken into consideration. It is naturally based on the ideas of Darwin who made no mention whatever in his work of sexual inversion or of similar phenomena. Krafft-Ebing's hypothesis is none the less in accord with Darwin's theories. "I know," said Darwin, "of authentic cases of the propensity to steal and to lie in families of even high social standing. Theft is a rather rare delinquency among the leisure class whence we cannot consider the existence of this tendency in two or three members of the same family as a simple coincidence." One can certainly reason similarly on the subject of sexual inversion.

There are certain observations which may serve to prove Krafft-Ebing's theory. He reports the history of a young man inflicted with sexual inversion who maintained that his father was also a Uranist. Another patient told Krafft-Ebing that his father had a very pronounced predilection for handsome and well-built men-servants.

N. N., of whom I have spoken in the preface, writes me as follows: "I have helped myself to many books in my father's library. He had the habit of making marginal notes and these —I was greatly struck by them—almost always pertained to passages concerning sexual inversion. My father had five children in a short while; he, therefore, was not impotent, and I do not claim to remember that he was a sexual invert. But I have a strong suspicion that one of my near relatives was a sexual invert, and that is why I think my father was so interested in the question."

The case reported by Lucas is particularly interesting; it deals with heredity in pederasty. A very good cook had a wild passion for women and at the same time a desire for pederasty; his natural son who lived far from his father and who did not know him had the same passion for the two sexes. Finally, we may say that the disease of the Scytheans was according to Herodotus considered hereditary.

Other proofs of the role of heredity in sexual inversion are furnished by the existence of this disease in too close marriages, or its simultaneous development in two brothers. I know two brothers inflicted with sexual inversion; another similar case has been communicated to me by a person whose word is not to be disputed. Two Uranists each have a brother presenting complete sexual anesthesia. Sometimes the sisters of these patients are found to evince an indifference and a remarkable aloofness towards men. In a case of Krafft-Ebing's, the patient's sister felt no desire at all for men and was in love with some of her female friends.

There are also cases in which other morbid perversions of sex exist in several members of the same family. A sadist whom I treated had a brother who very clearly resented the same sadistic tendencies. While one loved to beat his wife until she cried with pain, the other had a passion for ejaculating in his wife's face, feeling intense satisfaction when this act made her cry. Another patient was seized with genital excitement when he saw hens killed; his father had the singular passion for violently binding the hands of young women and of young girls.

Ribot, who attributes very great importance to heredity, insists on the hereditary transmission of sexual anomalies and cites a great many examples, among others that of Pope Alexander VI and of his children. The Pope was called Roderigo Borgia, and descended on his mother's side from the celebrated family of Borgias whose name he later assumed. As Cardinal and Pope, Alexander was notorious for his life of dissipation; of his children, the most well-known are Caeser and Lucrecia Borgia.

After this study of the theories relative to the influence of heredity, I have only to say a few words about an opposite theory, that of Schopenhauer's. According to him Uranism like all other natural phenomena has a determined goal. This opinion was rightly opposed in a work devoted to the critical study of Schopenhauer's works. The existence of homosexual love at all times is, for Shopenhauer, the proof that this phenomenon rises from human natures. He then cites the opinion of Aristotle that men, who have passed the age of fifty, can procreate only feeble offspring, and for that reason renounce reproduction. In order to further the conservation of the species and to prevent the procreation of miserable individuals the heterosexual urge is transformed at that age, according to Schopenhauer, into a homosexual urge. In this theory the first point is wrong; namely, that men of fifty cannot produce vigorous children. But the principal error exists in the hypothesis that homosexual tendencies always appear in old men. We have seen that when these tendencies exist in old men they do so from childhood. When they appear towards the age of fifty or later their existence must be considered as the sign of the beginning of a cerebral affection.

The basis of the theory announced recently by Gyurkovechky is as wrong as that of Schopenhauer's hypothesis. Gyurkovechky supposes that under normal physiological conditions desire disappears in old age. Men then become less delicate and he can have intercourse with persons whom he would not have approached before. This abasement, this physiological disappearance of desire, prepare the field in which sexual inversion may gradully develop. In this group Gyurkovechky places those individuals who after having led a normal life during many years later become pederasts, exhibitionists, etc.

After all these considerations I wish to give my theoretic explanation of sexual inversion. Most of the foregoing theories have the fault of not taking into consideration the analogy which exists between the sexual instinct and the other functions.

To understand the homosexual urge we should consider the genital instinct not as a phenomenon apart from the other functions but rather as a psychic function. The morbid modifications of the genital instinct would appear to us less incomprehensible if we were to admit that almost all the other functions whether physical or psychic may be susceptible to similar modifications. The sexual anomalies strike us as singular because most individuals who possess the attributes of the masculine sex have a sexual urge for women. But one must not be led astray by the frequence and regularity of this

phenomenon. From a teleological point of view, that is from
the point of view of the reproduction of the species, we consider natural the urge that the normal man feels for woman.
Still in certain pathological conditions the organs do not meet
the end assigned to them. The teeth are meant to grind food
yet there are men who have not teeth or who have very few
of them. The function of the liver is to secrete bile which is
diverted into the intestine, and in certain disorders of the liver
or of the bile ducts the bile is not secreted and does not reach
the intestine. The function of hunger is to remind the organism that it needs food. However, there are pathological states
in which the sensation of hunger is absent, although the
stomach continues to function normally. It is the same with
the absence of the sexual urge for women in a man possessing
normal genital organs. We can hardly establish a connection
between man's genital organs and his urge for women except
from a teleological point of view. Otherwise, one does not
see why man should be urged to have connections with
women since ejaculation of the sperm may be brought about
in quite other ways. It would be rather surprising to see the
genital instinct not presenting the same morbid anomalies as
the other functions, both physical and psychic. Its singular
importance and its social role ought not to make us consider
the sexual instinct as a phenomenon apart.

If the phenomena of sexual inversion appear to us most
striking, it is because from a social standpoint few psychic
troubles play as important a role as the aberrations of the
genital instinct. In all civilized countries this instinct has
remained hidden. The very singular impression which the
anomalies in question make on us when they are brought to
light is due to this mystery. This again is explained by the
fact that the sexual instinct is a psychic function which en-
tails the concurrence of another individual and because of this
acquires a particularly social importance. But from a phsysi-
plogic viewpoint the anomalies of the genital instinct do not
at all differ from those of the function of nutrition. If from
a social viewpoint great importance is not attached to the

latter anomalies it is because the regular accomplishment of this function does not require the concurrence of another individual.

After all these considerations it would be useless to enter into a detailed theoretic study of certain other manifestations even though sexual inversion, according to Westphal, is not strictly limited to the genital sphere. The phenomena of effeminacy is likewise very important. I shall only say that effeminacy may be treated in two ways: either the psychic functions of an individual are modified as the result of a homosexual urge, or effeminacy is congenital like sexual inversion itself. If we consider effeminacy as secondary, we shall find a certain analogy in this hypothesis, with what takes place after castration; here, following a local mulitation, the genital senses are extinguished and the phenomena of effeminacy, effeminate voice, etc., appear a short time after the operation.

Chapter X

DIAGNOSIS

**Methods of Approach; Dreams, Carriage, Voice, etc.; Differential Diagnosis;
Sex Act and Sex Urge; Pathology of Inversion.**

The diagnosis of sexual inversion may present many difficulties. A principal cause of error exists in the fact that it is very difficult to obtain the sincere and complete confidence of the patients. Many people still consider gleet or syphilis shameful, and for that reason fear to confess it; it is certainly still **more** difficult to obtain from such patients the confession of masturbation, for example, not to mention sexual inversion, which since it is quite independent of the will should not be considered a vice.

It is through a feeling of shame that the patient hides his sexual life and confesses only the least possible particulars. Therefore I question in detail all the patients of mine in whom I suspect an anomaly in their genital life. A great many of these patients continue to hide the truth and to reply negatively to questions asked them. If they confess their impotence with women they avoid saying that the cause—as is often the case—is sexual inversion. Sometimes they are held back by a sense of false pride, sometimes they wish to fool

themselves as to the seriousness of their condition, at other
times the questions are not well put by the physician; there
are then many reasons for these patients to hide their sexual life. To all these reasons we must add still another: it is
the lack of confidence of the patient in the doctor's discretion.
According to certain Uranists, this is the principal reason,
and many fear that the indiscretion of the physician may lead
to law suits. Westphal is also of this opinion. Most Uranists
are of the opinion that there is nothing to do against their
sex anomaly, and they believe it is useless to consult a doctor.

There are means by which the doctor may gain the confidence of his patients. To cause the feeling of shame to disappear he may begin by assuring his patient that the phenomenon in question is natural, that it may exist in every-
body, and that it is absurd to hold a man responsible for a
disease. But the surest means of preventing the patient from
disillusioning himself on the situation is to ask him clear and
precise questions. Sometimes it is also effective in hastening
the confession of the patient to relate to him several examples
of sexual inversion. In apparent cases of sexual inversion
the patient can hardly fool himself if he is asked the following
question: "Do you feel or have you ever felt a desire for
men?" or: "Is your desire for men stronger than your desire
for women?" Often the physician will thus obtain responses
which will reveal to him the existence of an aberration of the
genital senses. The doctor who sees many patients is surprised to find that he obtains a clear reply to his precise questions while with general questions he would not be able to
evoke any response whatever from the same persons.

Another means of learning the truth consists in questioning
the patients about their dreams. A very important fact,
which the reader may glean from most of the observations, is
that erotic dreams deal with the same subject matter that the
sexual instinct does during the waking state. There are exceptions to this rule. A Uranist for whom while awake the
opposite sex had no attraction whatever had pollutions on
several occasions while dreaming of accomplishing the sexual

act with women. But in most cases his dreams dealt with
sexual acts performed with men.

Apart from these exceptions, it is an established fact that
individuals tainted with sexual inversion have dreams similar
to their morbid dispositions. It may be then understood why,
in interrogating patients about their dreams, one could obtain
very valuable information, insofar as the patients feel less
restrained to relate their dreams than facts relating to their
conscious sexual lives. It seems to me therefore that we
should begin our examination by first inquiring about the patient's dreams and then passing to the individual's real sexual
life. Whatever the questions asked of the patient, the physician should not be content with general replies or those lacking in precision which often mislead. It often happens that
when, as the result of rational psychic treatment, the perversion no longer exists in the patient while awake his erotic
dreams continue to be about men. On the other hand, Dessoir has cited a case to me in which an individual who was
inflicted with sexual inversion always dreamed of women.

In this respect, experience plays a considerable role. An
experienced observer can make a diagnosis with entire certainty without submitting the patient to a very detailed cross-
examination. In certain cases it is easy to recognize a Uranist
but at other times the diagnosis demands a rather long investigation. Uranists who claim that they can recognize each
other at first sight, believe that it is a peculiarity, a sort of
sympathy independent of any organ of the senses, but that fact
is not true and such instantaneous recognition is only a legend
current in Uranist circles.

It is none the less true that there are signs by which one
can recognize almost for a certainty the Uranist without submitting him to a detailed examination. The ancients were
not ignorant of these external signs in Uranists and there are
passages in Aristotle, Polemonus, Lucan and Aristophanes,
relative to their walk, their voices, and their looks. I have
already spoken, in Chapter III, of the importance of these
symptoms in general, and in particular of their attitudes and

movements. In recognizing a Uranist there is a certain trick which normal individuals in their affairs with Uranists can acquire rather easily. The employee and agents of the police have told me that they recognize Uranists at first sight and that they are rarely mistaken.

I have already studied the glances of Uranists which according to them plays so great a role in their mutual recognition and I have proved that there is nothing mysterious about them. One must therefore accept with the greatest reserve the statement of the Uranists that they can recognize each other at first sight. This claim that they can recognize each other in any nation of the world whether in the city or in the country is mostly legendary.

I know two Berlin Uranists who separately made themselves known to me; they lived in the same society and neither suspected that the other was a Uranist. Both however affirmed that they could recognize Uranists with mathematical certainty at first sight. One cannot therefore put oneself too much on guard against very rapid diagnoses. I have been cited the case of a young man of twenty who is very effeminate but who sexually is absolutely normal. I do not know this case in detail but what I have been told of this man certainly proves that he possesses normal genital senses; however, he is suspected to be a Uranist, for his effeminacy is extreme and all his attitudes, all the movements of his hands, body and head are very much like those of a woman.

If one wishes to diagnose sexual inversion by a study of movements one must choose the moment when the individual lets himself go, when he does not know that he is being observed. One of the most important signs was pointed out to me by N. N.: when the Uranist believes he is not being observes, he looks by preference in the direction of the genitals, especially when uncovered. N. N. attributes to this significant very particular importance. There are some Uranists who admit that they have never been recognized by other Uranists, and cannot recognize them at first sight. Most claim that they can recognize Uranists by simply looking at their photographs. I have made on this subject a series of experiments with photographs which I have shown to Uranists. The results were very contradictory; however, the photographs of two very prominent men were indicated by almost all the Uranists as being among them. I have been able to observe that Uranists consider as being of their number those men who in their photographs look quite to the side. I attribute this to the fact that Uranists consider as homosexuals those individuals who in passing them in the street throw them a sidewise glance. I believe I ought to now stress the numerous errors made in diagnosing cases of sexual inversion. In a case of gonorrhea in a homosexual, Westphal wrongly believed that he should reject all suspicion of Uranism.

In fact Uranists may have gonorrhea and I have encountered this disease in an individual who had intercourse only with men. This individual had relations with a man who was infected by another. He was infected in his turn, *membrum suum ponens juxta membrum alteris.* What is more, the infection may be produced very easily in psycho-sexual hermaphrodites who occasionally have intercourse with women. Married men and even those who have children may nevertheless be tained with sexual inversion. First of all, they may be psycho-sexual hermaphrodites; secondly, erection and ejaculation in the wife's vagina may be obtained by certain artifices such as the mental representation of a man. I therefore believe that it is possible for Uranists to have children and suspicions of infidelity on the wife's part are not always true. There are Uranists who even think that they can rid themselves of their passion through their love for their children and who do all they can towards the goal. A *polentia coeundi et generandi* ought to be strictly differentiated from the normal genital instinct. To assume the presence of a normal genital instinct it is not sufficient that the individual be able to practice coition: he must also feel an urge for that sexual act. When an individual tainted with sexual inversion has coition with his wife, he is not yet cured of his disease as a great many doctors believe.

Krafft-Ebing stresses the difficulties in diagnosing psychic hermaphrodism which is often mistaken for acquired sexual inversion in which traces of the old normal sexual instinct may persist. I not only admit these difficulties but I even believe that in acquired inversion there is psycho-sexual hermaphrodism and that it is only from a theoretic and clinical point of view that it is important to differentiate the two forms. At times this differentiation presents considerable difficulties since in a great many cases described as acquired inversion with the conservation of traces of the heterosexual urge the origin of the perversion may be traced to childhood years. One ought always to try to make the practically identical diagnoses of congenital and of acquired hermaphrodism. Krafft-Ebing likewise stresses the necessity for a differential diagnosis of congenital sexual inversion and of acquired inversion. This diagnosis is based on the presence or absence of the heterosexual urge before the appearance of the inversion of the genital senses.

It is useless to insist on the differential diagnosis of sexual inversion and of certain other disorders which may easily be mistaken for the former. I will cite a case throwing light on this point. It deals with a man who is excited by the sight of boys of ten or twelve; he has erections, but he finds it absolutely impossible to have sexual intercourse with men. The patient in question thinks that his excitement is caused by the feminine traits of the boys who, by an association of ideas, recall to him the form of women. Under these conditions, the case ought to be considered as dealing with an hyperesthesia of the genital senses but not at all with sexual inversion. Sexual inversion ought also to be closely distinguished from psychic affections in which a lunatic thinks he is a woman, dresses like a woman, and wishes to have intercourse with men.

The question whether sexual inversion is or is not a morbid phenomenon is easier to explain when one examines those cases of pure sexual inversion in which there is not a trace of an urge for women. We ought to ask whether this entire absence of sexual desire for women is a pathological phenomenon.

Hammond thinks that there are normal men who never had a sexual desire. This assertion is a little personal and arbitrary for we may maintain that a person who has never felt sexual desires are far from normal. I believe that the notions of health and of the normal state imply the existence of those psychic and physical functions which are necessary for the conservation of the individual and of the race. We certainly do not consider as healthy those persons whose psychic and physical functions are not sufficient for the maintenance of life. When a person can no longer take food we have a morbid phenomenon for the quite simple reason that the functions of nutrition are necessary for the conservation of the individual. In agreeing with Lauer that the role of the individual in good health is to perpetuate the species for the duration of his life we ought to consider as diseased all men who are incapable of contributing to the propagation of the species. Impotence may suffice in itself to place the individual into a pathological group provided of course that he is of an age in which reproduction is normally possible.

According to this we could not therefore class as morbid the absence of a normal sexual urge since in its absence reproduction is still possible. In fact it happens that Uranists who have an urge only towards men, nevertheless have intercourse with women and practice normal coition for social reasons, or for the purpose of having children. We ought to consider the absence of heterosexual desires morbid even when the possibility of practicing normal coition exists.

Let us try to explain this point by an analogy for it is thus that we can make clear what we understand by the terms "sound" and "morbid." The conservation of the species is for us a function of the sound individual, as well as his own preservation. Following this line of reasoning we see that the share of nutrition is necessary to the organism for the conservation of the being and the need of food appears in him in the form of a physiological phenomenon known as the appetite. When the appetite is entirely lacking we are already dealing with a morbid phenomenon whether the organism receives its necessary quantity of food or not.

In pursuing this analogy between the appetite and sexual desires we find that the existence of a sexual urge is necessary for the individual's well-being and for his being considered normal, and we are led to consider as pathologic those cases in which this urge is absent. The morbid fact exists none the less whenever the normal sexual urge is replaced by a homosexual urge. All these considerations of the possibility of accomplishing coition in the absence of heterosexual desires have nothing to do with those cases of sexual inversion in which the impossibility of coition is the consequence of the horror for women. It deals therefore very clearly with morbid impotence.

There may be a reason for not considering sexual inversion as morbid. It is a known fact that a great many Uranists experience during the accomplishment of the homesexual act the same well-being that normal men feel during coition. On the other hand when a Uranist in order to practice coition with a woman makes use of certain artifices, such as the mental representation of a man, the sexual act greatly fatigues him. Forced and often repeated coition may even have a disagreeable effect on the health so that from the standpoint of the conservation of the individual homosexual relations between Uranists are rather to be recommended. On the whole, it deals with an act which is favorable to the conservation of the species. In adhering to the terms of this dilemma one may ask whether the condition of the Uranist ought to be called pathologic, since the individual tends in the first place to preserve himself.

But this contradiction is only apparent and is due to the confusion that is frequently made between the sexual urge and the sexual act; in the question before us, we have only to deal with the sexual urge. The act which results from a morbid desire may very well be considered as good for the health through the digestion of spicy foods may awaken the appetite in certain cases of dyspepsia, it is none the less true that dyspepsia is a pathological phenomenon. Likewise, an act based on a morbid sexual urge may be good for the health of the individual but for that reason the urge does not become normal. It follows, that by representing the sexual urge not as destined for the satisfaction of the individual but for the propagation of the species, we are obliged to consider sexual inversion as pathologic, and individuals presenting this phenomenon as unhealthy.

If we admit that the existence of a normal sexual urge is the condition *sine qua non* of a healthy and normal condition we ought to inquire whether sexual inversion is compatible with that condition. The two questions are to be strictly separated, for we see that there are cases of phycho-sexual hermaphrodism and characterized by a desire for man and woman. An essential condition for the normal state, namely, the desire for women, exists in these cases; and one ought to ask whether, because of the simultaneous existence of a homosexual urge, one ought nevertheless to consider these facts as pathologic.

The problem is difficult to solve and to do so, there should be, I believe, a continuation of the analogy with the appetite. There are people who have a singular taste for substances which do not enter the normal diet. This is the case with chlorotics, hysterical persons, and pregnant women, who sometimes hungrily devour chalk, pieces of brick, coffee beans, etc. We consider such tastes as pathologic because the substances involved do not constitute the material which maintain the organism. Although the same persons have an appetite for necessary food-stuffs at the same time, we nevertheless have the right to conclude that their unusual tastes are pathologic. From this viewpoint we ought also to qualify as pathologic those functions of the genital system which do not contribute to the preservation of the individual and the species simultaneously a condition which is essential to the health and to the normal state. Thus we are led to consider sexual inversion which does not at all contribute to the propagation of the individual as pathologic.

Other reasons may be cited which prove the pathological character of sexual inversion; but personally I think that these reasons are not unassailable. It is the habit to say that sexual inversion is generally observed in depraved individuals, who may at the same time present other stigmata of the degeneration of the central nervous system. This argument is not quite beyond objection for there are degenerates in whom sexual inversion is the only symptom of degeneration. If we wished to maintain that sexual inversion is a morbid phenomenon solely because the person presenting it belongs to a family of degenerates, we would be obliged to regard the act of eating a beef-steak as a symptom of degeneracy under the pretext that the individual eating the beefsteak is a degenerate. It is illogical to say that sexual inversion is a morbid phenomenon because it is met with in degenerate individuals. This reasoning may be right from a theoretic and teleologic standpoint, but it has not the importance attributed to it when we are concerned with determining whether such and such a phenomenon is pathologic.

It must also be granted that, in those cases in which there are clear signs of psychosis or of neurosis, we are easily tempted to consider sexual inversion as a symptom of a morbid state. Westphal has already dealt with this problem without deciding whether sexual inversion ought to be regarded as an isolated symptom or as a manifestation of a neuropathic or a psychopathic condition.

This reasoning by analogy leads us to believe homosexual urges are pathologic. Another problem now arises. In what group should we place those patients inflicted with sexual inversion? Ought we in the absence of other serious psychic symptoms to place sexual inversion in the group of nervous maladies or in that of mental disorders? We know that those hallucinations not recognized as such by the patient are often taken as a proof of mental derangement. Authorities do not agree on this point. Sanders considers these individuals as almost always inflicted with a psychic affection; while Krafft-Ebing does not think that a mental disease is always involved. He cites certain historic men who without being lunatics had hallucinations: Luther who threw his ink-stand at the face of the devil; Socrates who conversed with his demon; Mohammed, etc. If we adopt the same criterion, the perception of the morbid condition, for sexual inversion we would be led to assume the existence of a psychosis in almost all Uranists. It also happens that an individual convinced of his morbid nature and of his abnormal desires cannot conquer them and continues to be influenced thereby, while the illusion once recognized by the individual can no longer influence him. I believe that the Uranist very rarely considers his urge as unnatural and in this I do not share Westphal's opinion. N. N. is one of the rare Uranists in that he feels his condition to be pathologic.

I hesitate to say that the existence of sexual inversion in an individual is sufficient to indicate that the individual is inflicted with a mental affection. And to prove this point I find nothing better than my analogy between the sexual urge and the appetite. Certain authorities have rightly compared love with the sensation of hunger. Two sentiments, says Laurent, dominate every living being: hunger, which has as its purpose the preservation of the individual and love, which tends to the conservation of the species. Krafft-Ebing also compares the instinct of preservation with that of reproduction. "Life from a physiological standpoint comprises an instinct of preservation, and an instinct of reproduction. Illness does not create new instincts, as is wrongly supposed; it can only diminish or exaggerate or pervert normal instincts." But just as we have not the right to consider anyone a lunatic who has a particular taste for abnormal food, neither can we regard sexual inversion as a proof of a psychosis.

Besides all the differences established between a neurosis and a psychosis are rather arbitrary and what one regards as a neurosis is taken by another to be psychosis. From this arises many contradictions on the subject of sexual inversion, not only among different authorities, but in the same author. Westphal for whom sexual inversion is not a symptom of a psychopathic state nevertheless compares it to "moral insanity" which for us is a psychosis.

Starck rightly compares sexual inversion with hysteria or rather with certain phenomena which are manifested in the course of hysteria. It sometimes happens that certain sensary stimuli, certain odors for example, agreeable under normal conditions, become disgusting to an hysterical woman; and conversely, certain sensations repugnant to normal men are agreeable to those suffering from hysteria.

Chapter XI

TREATMENT

Prognosis; Theoretic Considerations; Doctor Sympathy; Environment and Education; Normal Coition; Marriage, Alcohol, etc.; Hypnotism, Medicine, etc.

We owe the gradual disappearance of the intolerance among physicians towards sexual inversion to Krafft-Ebing. Due to his research and his industry we are no longer quite so ignorant of the question as previously. The contempt with which the Uranist was regarded, a contempt which is still met today among men who are not acquainted with the latest •development of the question, tends to disappear. Gyurko-vechky rightly says that we doctors ought to avoid conventional lies and that we ought not to allow ourselves to be frightened by plain language in scientific questions, even when they deal with subjects which the public, as well as the doctors, consider indelicate. Casper justly observes that the sex life in all its phases belongs to the medical field. Let us also mention the remark made by Schuh on the occasion of a rectal examination. During this examination, several in the audience could not help making a movement of disgust which they betrayed by gestures of repugnance. Schuh said to them, "When I was studying surgery the latter was separated from medicine; physicians used to be comely gentlemen, while the surgeons were veritable pariahs. A doctor of medicine used to consider it beneath his dignity to introduce his finger into his patient's rectum; we were called and commanded to make that exploration, then we were treated like mud and thrown aside: but surgery has grown, and we are treated with respect!"

Apropos of sexual inversion this same sentiment of repugnance is still widespread, and a goodly number of doctors who write on this subject believe that they ought to excuse themselves to their readers for broaching such a subject. We even see an author like Hammond who after reporting two cases of inversion declares that he knows several others, but that his pen refuses to describe such crimes against morality and health. I consider all perverse actions which do not arise from a perversion of the sexual instinct as criminal. But when this perversion exists the impartial observer ought to regard the act not as criminal but as morbid. The pen of a physician and a conscientious writer ought not to refuse to describe the truth and less than all others Hammond, in a book dealing with impotence.

The prognosis of sexual inversion is far from being determined, although the disease is today considered curable in many cases. Sexual inversion is considered incurable in the Uranist world and there are in fact few of these patients who believe in the possibility of a cure. A Uranist wrote to Krafft-Ebing as follows: "We are generally considered ill and wrongly so, for if there are medicines for all diseases—medicinces which can cure or alleviate—nothing in the world will rid the Uranist of his unnatural desires."

The prognosis depends on a great many circumstances. Thus, psycho-sexual hermaphrodism calls for a much more favorable prognosis than pure sexual inversion. The prognosis for hermaphrodites depends on the intensity with which the hetero-sexual urge for women is manifested in them, and the more acute this urge is the better the prognosis. The prognosis depends further, on the duration of the morbid state; thus, when the sexual inversion is long standing it becomes inrooted and the prognosis becomes less favorable. The patient's environment likewise exercises a considerable influence on the prognosis.

It is more difficult to better conditions when the patient finds numerous occasions to have sexual relations with men. But the prognosis is made worse when the Uranist is attached to a man by a violent love; in this case the physician obtains with difficulty the least relief, besides it is rare that a Uranist will come to him in this condition for he is at the height of his happiness, provided his love is shared. Neurasthenia and similar diseases which are not rare in Uranists make the prognosis more difficult.

We ought to inquire first of all whether it is possible to treat the inversion of the sexual instinct therapeutically, and whether there is not the risk of causing the Uranist more harm than good in treating him.

If it is confirmed that in homosexuals the psyche is quite feminine and if we find that from childhood the Uranist's thoughts were of men not of women, the reply to this question is far from being certain. The entire life and habits of such patients are adapted to the ideas of sexual inversion in such a way that one is led to consider his love for man as natural much more so than the love he could feel for women. Our therapeutics would enforce in a nature essentially feminine a desire which would not be in harmony with the other inclinations. In trying to divert the sexual instinct of a declared Uranist—and one of an effeminate nature—towards women, we would simply throw his phychic life out of equilibrium. Is it our duty, have we the right to do that?

If we decided to lead the sexual instinct back to normal it seems to me indispensable that we should seek at the same time to modify the general psychic state to one of a more masculine nature. Theoretically it does not seem impossible, though it is hardly probable after the years of development involved.

Another objection to the treatment is the following: Ought

we not discard it because of the danger of the inheritance to nervousness which exist because of it? If one agrees with Krafft-Ebing who supposes that the inversion of the sexual instinct may be transmitted from father to son, if one accepts in general the fact of the inheritance of instincts and if one judges the Uranists to be degenerates, one cannot pass over this objection without the necessary preliminary examination. Even after the disappearance of sexual inversion there none the less subsists the possibility of its existence in the descendants. Ought one under these conditions allow Uranists to procreate? I believe that the physician will always be forced to cater to the patient's desires and try to cure a painful morbid condition. If the patient must later marry and have children that would be another question for whose solution the physician must give his advice, but which ought not to stop him from fighting an existing malady.

Outside of theoretic analysis we shall most often act differently under different circumstances. The majority of Uranists do not consider themselves ill and do not ask to be treated. Those who have recourse to doctors should by all means be treated by us. Sexual perversion is for them an abomination which may sometimes even lead to suicide and under these conditions, despite all theoretic considerations, we are obliged to intervene with our therapeutic treatment for the purpose of leading their sexual desires back to normal.

We shall not spend too much time over Hassli's words in praise of love among men, which he represents as a blessing to the state, and which he considers as the cause of the supremacy of ancient Greece in the arts and sciences. It is hardly necessary to stress the fact that Hossli labors under a misapprehension. It is wrong in this case to establish a relation between cause and effect. I ought nevertheless to declare that I find also quite false the opinion of those who see a casual relation between the decline of Greece and the existence of pederasty; the latter existed during the height of Greek glory as well as during its decline. We ought not allow ourselves to be turned aside by Hossli's considerations

from our duty to combat sexual inversion as far as the progress of medicine and hygiene permits us. I nevertheless do
not believe that we can very quickly succeed in completely
curing sexual inversion in the masculine sex.

The physician's task is not always the same. Sometimes
he must cause the acts to which the patient is forced by his
desires to disappear, but later he may consider modifying or
even suppressing the desire itself. Some Uranists find themselves impeded by certain social and legal restrictions in the
free play of their sexual instinct; they sometimes seek the
assistance of the physician, especially if their sexual urge is
hyperesthetic which is the case with many of them. They
do not seek to be led back to the desire for women. The majority of Uranists consider such a modification of their nature
as absolutely impossible but they would like to have their
homosexual urge lessened in intensity so that they would not
be continually obsessed by it. According to N. N. the hyperesthesia of the sexual instinct in Uranists may be the principal reason why so great a number of them pass their lives in
"dawdling." They are often too obsessed with their sexual
urge to apply themselves to regular occupations. It goes
without saying that there are exceptions to this rule. The
hyperesthesia of the sexual instinct in Uranists may be com-
bated by all the means employed against the hyperesthesia of
the heterosexual urge; to wit, bromides, hydrotherapy, baths.
psychic influences, etc. The last mentioned are very important, especially suggestion.

I know a Uranist, a cultured man, who was thrown into
violent despair by an unrequitted love and who worked hard
so as to forget his sexual thoughts. I believe that a certain
result may be reached by the systematic education of the
Uranist. They must be counciled against ever practicing
psychic onanism, against ever delighting voluntarily in these
thoughts, and to seek diversion in work and activity. If one
does not convert the Uranist into a normal being one succeeds
in diminishing the sexual urge, in combating the hyperesthesia

of the genital senses, and in this one renders a great service to many Uranists.

A second group of patients want a complete transformation of the perverse urge into the normal. This may be brought about only by an accomplished, conscientious and indefatigable doctor. He must first try to obtain his patient's unrestricted confidence. Hardly anyone obtains it beside his companions who understand his condition. If the doctor shows himself to be sympathetic it will not be long before he exercises an enormous influence.

Therapeutics must keep in view not only accidental causes and the pathologic symptoms but also the predisposition. We know that there is in almost all Uranists a predisposition which often precedes the active appearance of sexual inversion and we claim that Uranism evolves out of this. We should therefore use all the therapeutic agents which are usually employed against nervous predisposition. The treatment must evidently deal with the individual's entire constitution. From this point of view, good food, fresh air, and exercise have a therapeutic value; but one must bear in mind that they are accessory means which only aid the treatment.

From a prophylactic standpoint we should follow the advice of Krafft-Ebing and Tarnowsky. The latter advises in cases of sexual inversion in the early stages the shaping of the patient's environment in such a way as would direct his sexual activity in some direct channel. He claims that the parents and educators of youth should direct the feminine tendencies of the young boy into pleasant channels; they ought to ask whether there is not a more serious foundation for such peculiarities; and it is necessary under these conditions to restrain, as soon as possible the tendencies of this kind, to avoid their development which is rapid. These tendencies are shown by the pleasure certain boys experience in wearing women's clothes. One of Westphal's patients, who from the age of eight would wear his mother's clothes was severely punished by the latter for it. I doubt whether punishment is very effective in such violent desire. Tarnowsky be-

lieves that one should gently mock the child whenever he
shows predilection for the feminine toilette, and it is possible
thus to stop its development.   The accidental causes which
may under certain conditions lead to the appearance of sexual
inversion, especially mutual masturbation are liable to medical treatment.   All we could say in this connection arises from
the chapter of this book dealing with the etiology of the question.   It is important to determine whether it is not preferable
in view of avoiding mutual masturbation, that elder persons
should instruct the younger on the dangers of these practices.
That is a point which I wish to touch upon.   I know well that
it is very delicate for a parent as for an instructor to discuss
sexual questions with children.   However in order successfully to combat the inversion of the sexual instinct one must
commence early for he who is inflicted with it makes the cure
more difficult as he has more frequent intercourse with men.
It is therefore an important rule of therapeutics that one
should set to work as soon as possible and not to wait until
the patient is thirty, for example, to try to stem the tide of the
disease.   Most Uranists, as far as I have been able to con-
vince myself, think little of prophylactic treatment; one must
none the less lay stress on this point.   It is also important,
according to Tarnowsky, in cases of tendency to inversion to
prevent the sexual act as long as possible; that is an auspici-
ous condition for prognosis.   Hartman as well as most of
those who studied the development of the sexual instinct declared that the essential point is in impeding the precocious
appearance of the inversion as much as possible.   If it is
noticed that most Uranists have been conscious of the bud-
ding of their disease in childhood, before puberty, one is led
to ask whether the precocious genital development (together
with vague ideas about the sexual differences between man
and woman) may not cause the appearance of homosexual
tendencies.   Niemeyer categorically opposes complete and
prolonged separation of the sexes: he does not advise oppos-
ing early love for girls, provided the sexual tendencies be
kept down as much as possible.   The opinion of Tarnowsky

that education and environment exercise a great influence on the generative instinct which may or may not evolve normally, is difficult to prove; in fact, he has not proved his assertion. It is none the less true that these external influences may play a certain role and that therapeutics ought to take into account the opinions expressed from this point of view.

I believe it possible sometimes to attain good results when one begins the cure during childhood. But it seems doubtful to me, and Tarnowsky is of the same mind in this respect, that many young people inflicted with congenital perversion could become normal due to prophylactic measures.

An unfavorable environment exercises a dangerous influence over those individuals who are predisposed to sexual inversion. Tarnowsky stresses this point, and thinks that in schools where numerous pupils are brought together predisposed individuals may be accelerated to satisfy their inclinations by sexual perverts. Chevalier emphatically declares that certain institutions lend themselves particularly to the development of sexual inversion and that the boarding school as it exists in France should for this reason be abolished. It is quite urgent to remove the adult Uranist as much as possible from the society of other Uranists to avoid his having contact with individuals who awaken in him sexual desires. Here the treatment of homosexuals will sometimes fail. I know some Uranists who were eager to be cured but who could not abandon the society in which they found themselves. The treatment is particularly difficult when the Uranist is in love with another man. Since the relationship is generally passionate and dominates the Uranist's entire nature, one must not be surprised to encounter more difficulties here in modifying the sexual urge. It is a folly on the part of parents or friends to wish to separate lovers by creating difficulties for them; the obstacles far from separating them unite them more closely.

We are dealing not only with curing the patient of his urge for homosexual love but also with creating in him a normal

love for women; we therefore should not neglect other points
of essential importance. In particular the Uranist should
necessarily live among women and he should seek the company of a woman who has the talent to charm him and to cap-
tivate him by those qualities that are quite in acord with his
own nature. Tarnowsky believes that it is possible by forcing
regular coition with a woman to give birth to the normal
sexual urge in individuals naturally predisposed to sexual
inversion. He neglects to prove his statement.

We should at the same time avoid everything that tends to
maintain the homosexual habits of the Uranist; for example,
sexual ideas relating to men. To attain this end he should be
advised intelligently and in a manner acceptable by him: he
should not be simply told that he is not to think any more
of having sexual intercourse with men. It is necessary to
show him at the same time that this advice is given how he
is to avoid such thoughts.

Through an extraordinary hyperesthesia of the genital instinct Uranists are obsessed by sexual thoughts much more
than normal men. Their fixed ideas do not leave them. Their
sleep is troubled by erotic dreams in which all the roles are
played by men; while awake, they find themselves equally
obsessed. Even in the midst of occupations in which a normal
man would become completely absorbed the Uranist finds
himself suddenly seized by a sexual idea and gives himself
up to it, incapable of suppressing it. It seems that the more
the Uranist is troubled by his desire for fruit forbidden by
law and custom the less able is he to attain it. The patient
could obtain certain relief by gradually suppressing these
ideas. One must try from the beginning to make him understand that in exercising his will in constantly fortifying it he
will finally rid himself if not entirely, at least in great part,
of his state of hyperesthesia. He should above all force himself to shun homosexual ideas and never give himself up to
them voluntarily. I know a case of psychic hermaphrodism
in which the patient fell back into his inversion only when
from gaiety of heart he let himself be drawn: for example, he

would meet a man who pleased him and he would seek his company. But when he was forced to turn from his inclination by having intercourse with a woman who pleased him his perversion disappeared several hours afterwards.

It would be wrong to advise a Uranist to practice coition with a woman without at the same time explaining the reason to him. The Uranist properly so-called cannot practice coition without being filled with horror. Many of them who have tried it had to give it up because of the extreme disgust raised in them by sexual contact with a woman. I know some who, when the woman undressed herself, were seized with such horror at the simple idea of having contact with her that they would have done anything to escape. If under these conditions the physician advises him with no other explanation to practice normal coition, the Uranist would be right in believing that his real condition is entirely misunderstood. It amounts to the same thing as advising an ordinary man to practice sexual intercourse with men and no longer with women. There are some for whom an erection in the presence of a woman is impossible; for contact with a female body arouses in them such disgust that even while ardently imagining a man they cannot have an erection, and then one of the necessary conditions for coition is absent. Many Uranists have attempted the thing without having consulted a physician, and their attempts have almost always failed.

Failing in this they become deeply discouraged and are convinced that their sexual inversion is incurable. We saw that the Uranist is never thoroughly convinced that he may be cured of his unnatural urge; still it is necessary to avoid everything that may lessen the Uranist's desire to be cured.

If one wants to cure the Uranist it is the urge itself which must be considered and not his unnatural behavior. One must try to replace a morbid urge by a normal urge, however it is not coition itself that one should consider the essential goal. Coition is certainly among the secondary causes favoring the appearance of normal desire, although it in itself is possible only through artificial means, such as thinking of a man; but it is always wrong to advise a Uranist to have intercourse with women, as long as he is not fully prepared to follow this advice. Each failure lessens his courage and his faith in a cure.

It should be emphasized that Uranists who are hermaphrodites from a psychological standpoint often cannot have promiscuous relations with women; only one may have the power of exciting him. There are similar cases in heterosexual love: there are individuals who can have intercourse only with a certain type of woman. Here is what Furbinger says in his "Impotence" regarding these remarkable cases: "There are certain rare forms of impotence, which are difficult to explain, and which perhaps belong to the field of sexual perversion; there is therein a feeling of disgust for woman, a feeling which entirely prevents erection, and which can be explained neither by physical imperfection, nor by the presence of anything repulsive, nor by the absence of beauty in the woman. Sometimes the irony of destiny causes the husband to seek in vain for this charm in his wife, while he finds it in courtesans. Such are cases of relative impotence." This point should be taken in all seriousness since different authorities agree that repeated failures in the attempt at normal coition favor the inversion. It is therefore to be expected that when we deal with such psychic hermaphrodism the patient may not succeed when this condition is not met with and he may finally become discouraged.

Outside of this feeling of discouragement and despair which result from failure in coition, the physician should recall the fact that coition with women causes extreme fatigue in the real Uranist. He is exhausted by it. Most Uranists declare that the enjoyment and well-being resulting from simple masturbation are for them preferable to coition. When they succeed in the latter there is always lacking the voluptuous sensations and state of satisfaction which normally follow it. On the other hand, intercourse with a man completely satisfies them and they are strengthened by it. The nervous depression which follows coition with women, may attain such proportions that the physician should reflect deeply before recommending repeated intercourse with women to his patient. When the Uranist accomplishes the act of coition it does not mean that a therapeutic result is reached; most Uranists on the contrary turn from women with disgust as soon as the act is finished and doubt that they could do it again. It is so even when Uranists experience a desire for women before coition. However, they are much more upset when they feel disgust for women after coition especially in those cases in which the act is practiced without desire and by artificial means.

We said that certain Uranists seek to have relations with women sometimes when intoxicated. I know a good many who through the use of alcoholic drinks have coition; despite that, they never have complete satisfaction for voluptuous sensations are lacking. Other Uranists get an erection and an ejaculation in their relations with women by thinking of men.

It is not only because the Uranist feels no desire whatever for women and because normal coition is repugnant to him that it is difficult for him to follow the advice of practicing this act; another difficulty lies in the fact that it is hardly possible to find a woman to suit him. It is clear that no honest woman would consent to have sexual intercourse with a Uranist; on the other hand, it would be dangerous to take him to prostitutes who would perhaps succeed only in exaggerating the disgust which he already feels for women. However if a woman is not found to suit him and who could lead him back to a normal path there is no hope for a cure. I believe that in Schreink-Notzing's well-known case, the Uranist with whom it deals would not have been cured had he not met a woman with whom he fell in love and whom he married. It is not hard to conceive how difficult it is for the physician to give any advice whatsoever when a Uranist consults him regards marriage. In fact, it would be wrong to consider marriage as the universal remedy in such cases as it is for others.

The husband would generally cause his unhappiness as well as his wife's if they marry before a complete cure of his homosexual tendencies were affected. "I ought to say, in honor of women and to the shame of our sex, that in many unhappy households the unhappiness is the work of the husband." Such is Most's opinion in his book "Love and Marriage." I believe that, in our special case, the Uranist would have to reproach only himself for marrying despite his Uranistic tendencies.

It goes without saying that masturbation should be forbidden to patients inflicted with sexual inversion. Masturbation with ideas of men is to be greatly feared, for it accustoms the nature of the patient to his morbid idea. There is hardly need to explain why masturbation ought to be rigidly suppressed; it is a known fact that therein lies an infallible means of bringing on nervous troubles and that it indefinitely defers any chance of success in the attempting of normal coition.

Hypnotic suggestion has been used in the psychic treatment of sexual inversion. This would seem natural to all those who make use of suggestion and who know the numerous works of Liebault, Bernheim, Forel, Krafft-Ebing, Obersteiner, Dessoir, Sperling and others. Under certain circumstances an intelligent application of suggestion undeniably gives good results. Cases mentioned by Krafft-Ebing, Schrick-Notzing and Ladame furnish proof of it. All I can say is that according to my own experiments, if a profound hypnotic sleep can be induced one may diminish the influence of the morbid urge by means of post-hypnotic suggestion, to drive out in part the constant image of man which haunt the patient and subsequently to make the need of the abnormal sexual act less frequent. I likewise caused the appearance of heterosexual ideas by means of suggestion. One should not expect to obtain these results in a day or two, and what is more, good results are obtained only when a deep hypnotic sleep has been induced.

One should not expect even where the latter condition is filled that it is easy to suggest a normal sexual urge to patients; in general they postpone their visit to the doctor as much as possible; their morbid inclination becomes so deep-rooted that it dominates their personality entirely. I treated a philologist inflicted with sexual inversion. I was able to induce in him a profound hypnotic sleep; but each time that I suggested that he go an hour later to a woman, I encountered the most obstinate resistance. Whenever I suggested to him that he should have relations with the woman I was certain to receive the following reply: "But it is not yet time. I have yet an hour before meeting this lady." This subterfuge and others of the same kind show in a very characteristic way that the fear of being found in contact with a woman dominates the Uranist. It makes him seek every possible means of evading such contact even when he is plunged in hypnotic sleep.

The most ardent champions of the use of medicines are in accord that in the treatment of the Uranist not medicines but psychic means should be used. Inclinations and emotions are overcome not by the use of hydrochloric acid or the juice of the aloe; they should be fought with elements of a psychic order like their own. Even Marcus Aurelius was acquainted with this truth.

It has been sometimes asked whether castration rids the Uranist of sexual perversion. Meyer answers in the affirmative; Westphal in the negative. Theoretically I do not believe that we could expect good results from it. A patient one day came to ask me whether he ought to be castrated and he depended upon my reply for the performance of the operation. I could not advise him truthfully. Joeger quite recently claimed that this means should be recommended by the State. If the State considers the unnatural act of Uranists as dangerous to its own safety it has only to execute them as quickly as possible. From a medical standpoint these means would be somewhat too drastic.

Chapter XII

LEGISLATION

Pederasty and Law; Sex Acts Punishable; Penal Codes and Inversion; Sexual Acts Between Men; Modification of Codes; Legal Theories; Unnatural Acts; Results of Laws; The State and Uranism.

Legislation relative to homosexual intercourse varied in history. Among the Jews pederasty was punishable with death. We do not know whether this passion was legally suppressed in ancient Greece. According to Ramdohr in Athens homosexual love between free citizens was restricted by law. One of the laws of Solon forbidding pederasty among slaves seems to indicate that legally this custom among citizens was not suppressed. Solon and his successors punished seduction, violence and rape in the love between men; one had to prove that this love was always unselfish on both sides. The following is what Aeschinus said, in his discourse against Timarcus, "We knew old men and young people who in their time were loved for their beauty or who are still loved today; but these cannot be reproached with what we reproach Timiarcus. Athenians! you knew Criton, Pericles, and many others; they were of great beauty and they had lovers, people full of decency and honor. I do not find fault with a reasonable love and I do not claim that all good-looking young

200

people whom we love are prostitutes; I myself avow having
written love poems and having been in love. The love for
young, good-looking and modest boys indicates a sociable
and humane heart; but he who sells his favors for money, I
hold as a depraved and debauched individual. It is honorable
to inspire one with a disinterested love; but it is shameful
to make it a source of riches. The law further forbids speaking in public to whomsoever has struck his father or mother,
dissipated his paternal heritage or given himself up to debauchery for money." A citizen who prostituted himself lost
his citizenship. He who violated or seduced the innocence
of young boys was severely punished (Ramdohr). Among
the ancient Greeks love for men was held contemptible when
ever it presented no moral element, and consisting only of
physical desires.

In ancient Italy pederasty was considered a crime and was
punishable with death. Among the Teutons unnatural matings were considered before the introduction of Christianity
as a crime punishable by death. After the introduction of
Christianity pederasty was always considered a crime. The
opinion of the Jews prevailed over that of the Greeks. The
penal code of Charles V's punished pederasty with behead-
ing. But in general the means for suppression of pederasty
became more moderate with time until today intercourse between men does not even come within the jurisdiction of the
law of certain states unless it is accompanied by particular acts,
such as violence for example. This is the case with Holland,
Italy and France. The Code Napoleon abrogated all penalties on this subject and a similar situation subsisted in several
German states until the founding of the Empire, when the
question was definitely decided for all of Germany. Pederasts
incurred no punishment whatever in Bavaria or in the King-
dom of Hanover. In Bavaria the police intervened only
when there was violence or when young people were seduced
for the practice of pederasty. According to Lisst a scientific
commission of Prussia formerly declared itself for the abrogation of articles establishing penalties for pederasty. The

canonic law continued to reprove unnatural matings. Today Germany punishes intercourse between men by law;
while it has no penalty whatever for the similar practice
among women. The Austrian Penal Code prosecutes women
by law also.

The penal code of the German Empire contains several
paragraphs relating to Uranists. The most important is as
follows: Unnatural matings between men or between men
and animals are punishable with imprisonment; they may also
cause the loss of civil rights.

One may here ask what is meant by the term *unnatural mating*.
The jurisdiction on this point is very questionable and often
contradictory. A rigorous distinction should be made between unnatural mating and the obscene acts involved. In
the text of the old penal laws the term unnatural mating
had an even more obscene meaning than in the present code.
The reasons which motivated the provisions of the German
code explain them from the standpoint of sodomy and
pederasty.

According to the jurisprudence of the law-courts all the
sexual acts between men should not be ranged among unnatural matings; only those acts presenting a certain analogy
with natural coition are considered as such. It is not necessary for *membrum in anum* nor even that the penis be introduced
into any cavity whatsoever of the man's body to have the act
fall under the law. For example, a decree of the Tribunal of
the Empire declared that the action of rubbing one's member
against another man's thigh should be considered similar to
coition and consequently punishable by law. Neither need
there be ejaculation; an act may be punishable even before
orgasm takes place. The court also established the possibility of punishing only one of the culprits and of acquitting
the other; for example, when the act is performed upon a
minor or upon a person who is asleep.

The Tribunal of the Empire established in a decisive manner the difference between unnatural matings and obscene
acts, which difference was discussed before at the time of the

reenacting the law.   Thus: the judgment of the court in the
first instance, which punished by law an individual who simply masturbated beside another was annulled by the Tribunal
of the Empire; this act before being considered by it as an
obscenity but not as an unnatural mating.   Masturbation of
one man by another and mutual masturbation are not punishable
when not accompanied by circumstances which recall the act
of coition.   In this case the distinction is evidently arbitrary;
the judge has to determine whether under such circumstances
render the act comparable to coition.   According to Oppen-
heim simple embraces in mutual masturbation are not sufficient to make the act fall under the application of the law:
on the other hand, rubbing the penis against the body of an
individual is punishable.   The individual who voluntarily
gives himself to an unnatural act incurs the same penalty as
his accomplice even when he does not satisfy his own passion.

The application of the penalties enacted by the law may
seem very simple; but in practice, this application is difficult.
When there has been *membrum in anum* the solution of the
problem is simple.   It becomes more complicated in the most
frequent case of placing the member against some part of
the other's body.   In this case, the application of the penalty
depends upon the friction which has been exercised.   The fact
that the bodies had simply lain next to each other does not
involve the application of the penalty.   If besides, there was
a rubbing, that is to say a movement of the two bodies or of
one of them the act would be open to the law because it could
be likened to coition. Let us now imagine the attempt to make
the accused declare before the court whether or not he had
made such a movement.   This proof seems to me to be so
difficult to establish in practice that I cannot get myself to
believe that it could serve as a basis for an equitable judgment.   It is hardly possible to interpret the law as according
immunity to intercourse between men for in spirit the article
of the law in question punishes precisely this relation.   There
is not unnatural mating when a man inflicted with sexual inversion performs the sexual act with another man.   This act

is just as natural as that which a man having normal desires for woman accomplishes with her.

Article 183 of the Penal Code is also of importance. "He who by obscene acts has caused a public scandal shall be punished with two years in prison or a fine of a maximum of $1,000. To imprisonment may be added the loss of civil rights." This article is aimed at those contacts made in public by Uranists wherein they touch the genitals of men and in practice it has often been interpreted in this sense.

Article 180 of the Penal Code deals with procurers: "He who by profession or through avarice has by his enterprise favored prostitution, or has furnished the occasion for it shall be punished with imprisonment as procurer." The court recognized expressly that this article could receive its application in connection with intercourse between men. It has been applied to an individual who rented a room to pederasts. The accused maintained, in his defense, that there was question only of intercourse between men: the court did not accept this excuse. The Code also contains other provisions relative to homosexual relations which I shall not stress because their interpretation does not present any difficulties.

We must examine article 51 which reads as follows: "No penalty shall be brought against any one who while committing a reprehensible act is in a state of dementia or who is inflicted with a disease of the volition which deprives him of his free will." If we deal with serious psychic disorders, as in paralytic dementia or if we can consider the homosexual urge as the psychic equivalent of an attack of epilepsy it becomes evident that the acts which procure this satisfaction incur no penalty whatever. But cases are relatively rare in which one can liken sexual inversion to grave psychic troubles. Without doubt competent medical authorities declare that sexual inversion is a pathological condition. Tarnowsky Krafft-Ebing, Gley and many others even assert that this phenomenon is always or almost always part of a symptomatic complex determining degenerates. In most cases we indeed find other undeniable symptoms of nervous and psychic

troubles. The Uranist's apparent healthy condition never mis-
leads a competent physician and does not hinder him from assuming the existence of other symptoms. He wll not consider
a normal intelligence, or one above the normal or the various
talents as a sign of health in the Uranist.

Krafft-Ebing rightly said that one is always in the presence
of morbid disorders when treating a Uranist which according
to the interpretation made of article 51 should receive the
benefit of immunity. This article truly lends itself to an extraordinary broad interpretation. We cannot count sexual
inversion as one of the morbid disorders of the will but nothing can stop us from considering it as a state of dementia,
and dementia according to article 51 is capable of very broad
interpretation. Modern annotators of the Penal Code do not
seem disposed to consider cases of sexual inversion as being
directly aimed at by the law. In the spirit of the law, the
word "dementia" signifies disorder of the conscience only.
Insomuch as the individual is conscious of the situation and
is aware of the consequences of his actions the legal doctor
shows himself little disposed to admit a disorder of the conscience. Finally we should also determine whether this law
ought not apply to cases of sexual inversion; it considers not
guilty those individuals who have performed an act under the
influence of an irresistible force. We here face a two-fold
difficulty: on the one hand, the expression irresistible force
generally means a physical force, and in fact physical force
alone has been considered in the application of the Code up to
the present; on the other hand, it would be impossible in dealing with a psychic phenomenon to consider an internal urge
as a force since the idea of force signifies an exterior manifestation.

Blumenstock insists on the necessity of determining in all
cases of sexual inversion the extent of the individual's respon-
sibility. From his point of view this question should always
be stated and solved even when legal proceedings should have
for their object not only sexual acts but quite other illegal
acts, for sexual inversion is itself the symptom of a psychic

disturbance. We ought also to take into account a question raised by Furstner; it is that of feigning sexual inversion. According to this author it is to be expected that individuals who commit unnatural sexual acts and knowing that they are open to legal proceedings may feign troubles whose manifestations they have studied in advance, such as epileptic fits for example, hoping thus to avoid punishment.

The legal doctor's diagnosis encounters serious difficulties when it presumes an immissio penis in anum. For several centuries legal doctors have sought the signs whereby they could establish the proof of active or passive pederasty. Far be it from me to wish to deprecate their work, but it seems to me that they have rarely had the occasion to present their own observations. The signs which they indicated generally passed from the book of one author to that of another, without their saying whether they had made the observations themselves or whether they had borrowed them from others. If it were otherwise most of them, I am sure, would be forced to agree that all the signs attributed to passive pederasty are encountered only in a relatively few cases, and that consequently their absence could not imply the absence of pederasty. On the other hand, these same signs often occur in individuals who have never practiced pederasty so that nothing can legitimately be concluded from their presence.

Martial, in ancient times, Paul Zacchias in the seventeenth century, and more recently Tardieu have said that as a result of pederasty the anus takes the form of an infundibulum; besides, Tardieu discovers a sinking of the region about the anus and a dilation of that organ, the sphincter muscle being strained. Hofmann does not believe in the diagnostic value of these signs for the reason that the funnel shape and laxness of the sphincter depend rather on the individual's age and state of nourishment; what is more, it is beyond doubt that avowed passive pederasts often have an absolutely normal anus. I have been able to decide this myself at a criminal trial.

Friedrich based his diagnosis on the fact that immediately after the act the anus remains wide open, becomes inflamed, presents painful, tumored spots and sometimes bleeding fissures. He claims that the passive pederast's clothing and underwear should be examined at the same time, for he generally has an ejaculation during the act which is either spontaneous or brought about by masturbation.

As to the signs which should reveal the presence of active pederasty, Liman and Hofman value them very little. According to these authors the malformations of the glands described by Tardieu have no significance from the standpoint of a medico-legal decision. We must suppose that Tardieu and the other authors who have described these cases have forgotten that, independently of pederasty, the form of the gland varies greatly according to the individual. In certain cases the diagnosis could be based on syphilis and gonorrhea of the rectum. Symptoms of syphilis due to the *penis in os* have been discovered in the mouth. A Uranist under the care of Krafft-Ebing claimed that he has seen several cases of syphilitic ulcerations of the anus; and primary symptoms of the palatal arch of a young man whom other individuals were abusing *per os.*

After having stated the articles of the law relating to the sexual acts between men and having examined the manner in which legal doctors establish their diagnosis it remains for us to see whether the present provisions of the Code could not be usefully modified.

It is doubtless surprising to hear me propose if not the suppression of article 175, at least its modification, in that homosexual intercourse shall no longer be punishable. Article 175 likewise punishes fornication with animals; this question shall not be studied in this book. It would deal, therefore, from the standpoint of homosexual intercourse, with a simple modification of the paragraph and not with total suppression.

I understand that it is daring to speak in favor of a class of individuals among whom I have found the most consum-

mate liars and who by their repulsive manners in the street
and in public places often excite the disgust of honest people.
Indeed, there is a class of Uranists who merit no sympathy
whatever and for whom the penalties enacted by the Code
always seem too lenient. But they are not the only ones.
We must also consider all those who scrupulously hide their
condition and who allow nothing to be suspected by those
about them. In studying their character we would find many
reasons for pleading in their favor. These unfortunates, well-
deserving of sympathy, are very numerous, yet they find even
among those who could sympathize with them none capable
of pitying them. When one of them opens his heart and confides in you, rarely is your opinion of Uranists unchanged.
In observing them one becomes convinced that one is not
dealing with vicious desires that can be conquered by preventing their satisfaction; sexual inversion is indeed a pathologic urge, which takes possession of the entire individual,
and which becomes part of the person. Such a patient should
therefore be treated with impartiality. We should not permit
ourselves to enact unjust laws against Uranists, because of
the odious characters of some of them. The legislator and
the physician cannot deal with the problem until they become
familiar with both groups.

They who belong to the respectable group disclose themselves but seldom to persons who are not Uranists so
that it is easily understood why all men abnormal sexually
are habitually considered criminals. It is for this reason that
Uranists are forced ot secrecy. Let us not forget that there
are today, as well as there were in the past, Uranists who are
distinguished eminent men. I have already quited Winckelmann, Platen and Muret in this connection. We will discuss
the penalty incurred by what the Code calls unnatural matings, since in other countries this penalty does not exist. The
antagonism between the physician who considers only the
clinical side and the legal doctor, has been pointed out by
Tarnowsky. The legal doctor sees only a vice where the
other recognized a morbid psychic condition. But this antag-

onism is even more marked between the clinical doctor and the Penal Code. The physician considers a morbid sexual urge what the Code denounces as a misdemeanor or a crime. It is to be hoped that some day these contradictions will be reconciled with the progress of science and of humanity.

For all of these reasons it is not out of place to discuss the question and to inquire whether the provisions of the German Code with respect to homosexual intercourse ought not to be modified. A Uranist has proposed that only members of his class ought to judge cases of this nature. This may be only a joke. As long as unnatural matings shall be declared punishable by the provisions of the law and by the decrees of the Tribunal of the Empire, which base their decisions on the Penal Code, the personnel of the courts shall be absolutely immaterial. We would soon hear thieves and assassins claim, like the Uranists, the right to judge thieves and assassins under the pretext of equity.

Facts show us that this question could not be too deeply probed. Here, for example, is the case of a man of nineteen, executed in Paris for having violated and killed a little girl of four. There is one fact of the matter which I wish to recall; namely, several celebrated physicians, Lasegue, Brouardel and Motet, declared the accused to be entirely responsible, an opinion which Tarnowsky deplores as "a disgrace to science." Since savants could entertain such contradictory opinions, need I apologize for discussing impartially this problem?

Let us now inquire whether from the standpoint of the philosophy of Penal Law sexual acts between men should be penalized. There are three principal theories of penal laws; we shall not take the trouble to examine all those which have been propounded by different lawyers. The three theories are as follows: first, punishment proposes to prevent crime by frightening the criminal; second, punishment ought to atone for the crime; third, punishment ought to make the criminals better.

According to the first of these theories Uranistic practices should be punished to prevent Uranists from practicing them through fear of the punishment itself. There certainly exist some isolated cases in which the fear of punishment may prevent the perpetration of a sexual act; but these cases are relatively rare. Sexual desires are impetuous and such considerations are generally powerless to suppress them. On the other hand, it is probable that an individual who does not dare perform the sexual act with another man may gratify his desire in masturbation. Masturbation is just as disadvantageous in its own way to the individual as sexual intercourse among men. If these relations are replaced by solitary masturbation I do not see what advantage may accrue to the maintaining of morals. Moreover, for those few whom this urge, finally leading to the desire for another man, no punishment whatever can be strong enough to turn them from the homosexual urge; the aggravation of his desire makes every means of suppression illusory.

I find it even more difficult to base the penalty for unnatural matings on the theory of compensation. What ought to redeem the culprit? Evidently a misdemeanor. But the notion of a misdemeanor is quite relative and we cannot consider the sexual act of the Uranist as a misdemeanor since we consider the ordinary sexual act performed by a normal man and a woman as legitimate. In general men perform the sexual act with women not because they want children but because of an urge whose satisfaction they cannot resist. The Uranist does not do otherwise and consequently his sexual act is not unlawful. We therefore have no solid facts upon which the base the exact notion of misdemeanor. As soon as the urge attains a certain force it becomes impossible to combat it. The homosexual urge may be neither caused nor suppressed voluntarily. The individual who experiences it is therefore not responsible. Krafft-Ebing and all other impartial authors are firm in making this declaration. For those who take into account the exact nature of the problem the legend of vice and debauch clinging to this practice is no longer acceptable. Krafft-Ebing calls Uranists the disinherited children of Mother Nature. It may happen that some of them due to their will-power and their social ties may succeed in abstaining from pederasty or from the other sexual acts performed among men; but they are always aware of their weakness, and they are conscious of the impossibility of resisting their urge beyond a certain limit. Shaw and Ferris presented a typical example of it. The individual in question declared that he sought the aid of a physician because he believed himself no longer capable of resisting as he had up to that time. The patient was thirty-five years old, and he felt the urge developing in him with ever-increasing power.

It remains for us to examine the third theory which tries to make man better. Now, no one can believe that any punishment will cure individuals inflicted with sexual inversion of their malady. Those individuals who practice coition may possibly be improved through punishment, when there is only a criminal desire involved and when the individuals in question are urged on not by sexual inversion but by a purely criminal intent. But the more or less extended loss of liberty will never be able to cure the Uranist of his desires. Suppose a Uranist is incarcerated for some misdemeanor; this imprisonment will evidently not rid him of Uranism. I know several Uranists who have been imprisoned because they satisfied their desire. I do not know one of them in whom this punishment suppressed the disease or subsequently contributed to lessening its effect. The sexual urge is imperious in its will to subsist. Is this connection let me cite the case of a patient who was inflicted with a perversion of a peculiar type: he became sexually excited at the sight of white aprons. He shut himself up in a cloister in the hope of ridding him of this morbid condition through fasting and prayer. He failed to relieve himself: a cure is never brought about in this way.

Let us now consider in order the reasons for punishing unnatural matings. The most important seems to be the outrage towards morals. It has been claimed that in ancient Greece pederasty spread only during its decadence. This opinion is false: today, it is known that intercourse between men existed during the most flourishing periods of ancient Greece. It is impossible to establish the relation of cause and effect between the decadence of the Greeks and their love for young boys. Hossli goes too far in claiming that one of the causes of the grandeur of Greece was the habit among men practicing sexual intercourse. I believe he wrongly bases his opinions on the ideas of Sulzer who said that Greek artists owed their entire greatness to the free expansion of all the desires of their ego. It may be asked whether Sulzer really spoke of pederasty as Hossli seems to believe.

Normal coition of a man and a woman accomplished between four walls is legitimate and does not constitute an outrage towards morals. Why then should the sexual act of a Uranist's performed under the same conditions be so considered? What for one is moral appears to be immoral for another and the homosexual act may possibly be imputed as immoral solely because a minority practice it. Another motive which tends to prove its immorality and tilt the balance towards the necessity of punishment; namely, the contempt and disgust which this act excites in the people. This is due to the belief that the act is accomplished by *membrum in anum;* but this belief is not true as we have seen for this type of pederasty is rather rare among Uranists. There are in the intercourse betwen men and women certain practices which which are just as repellant as the sexual act between men. Pedication which is lawful and which is nothing else but the *membrum in anum mulieres* accedes nothing, from this viewpoint to the act of pederasty. Besides, the law also allows "caprophagie" which could not but excite repulsion. Normal coition presents nothing esthetic in itself and I believe that were we not accustomed to it through frequent practice we could not imagine a more repulsive act.

When homosexual acts become punishable by law the argument drawn from the contempt which they excite in public opinion loses all its values; for public opinion conforms to a certain point with the manner in which the law itself regards these things. On the other hand, the people's contempt for unnatural acts has been given among the considerations which have presided over the legislation of this special point. It is not possible to expect public opinion to turn about suddenly in abrogating all penal provisions: such a reversal could be brought about only gradually. A modification of the penal provisions would probably have a gradually ameliorating effect upon the social status of Uranists. It is quite certain that Uranism will never be considered a very good thing, but it is quite probable that the profound contempt with which the unfortunates who suffer from this disease are regarded will some day disappear. Besides, there is no doubt that even in countries where homosexual acts are not punished they are always held in contempt. This contempt is doubtlessly spread through international relations. I believe that the raising of Uranism in public opinion absolutely depends on its freedom from legal punishment. In France Uranists are not on a lower social level. There they are tolerated as they used to be tolerated in Hanover before the foundation of the German Empire, when they enjoyed complete immunity. The history of ancient Greece proves to us that a nation does not endanger its foundations because its people do not hold homosexual love in contempt.

The Bible reproves Uranism and we are conforming to the commandments of the Bible in our current legislation. If we direct all our steps along this dangerous path, we will be attacking many points of our social organization. The Mormons justify their polygamy by citing many passages in the Bible.

The evil results of homosexual intercourse and in particular of pederasty have been referred to in a great many old works according to which unnatural practices would have serious consequences for the health. Dohrn has gathered the opinions of different authors on this particular point and I have borrowed the following facts from his work. According to Nicholai, those individuals who practice pederasty suffer outside of local diseases a general weakness which especially affects the lower limbs; the sexual functions are paralyzed. According to Wildberg pederasty causes consumption. Henke claims that from it result phtisis and dropsy. Casper emphatically declares himself against the opinions of these authors; in his opinion, the pederasts whom he knew almost all enjoyed perfect normal health.

It is not quite right to believe that the satisfaction of the homosexual urge is detrimental to the health. The Uranists who find it impossible to satisfy their desires for a homosexual act become ill. When they are forced to practice coition with women they become impotent; and while potent, they find therein no satisfaction; coition exhausts them, and without a doubt, a frequent repetition of this act would impair their health. All those who have seen Uranists at first hand will agree with me that they constitute a class of individuals who are far from being weak. There are among them men of robust and vigorous health. When they appear ill or nervous it is probably due to forced abstinence rather than sexual excess. Their nervous system feels the effects of the social conditions in which they live; they unceasingly fear that their desires have been discovered; they painfully bear the injustice of the world which treats them as social pariahs. Sentiments of this kind evidently must react unfavorably on their general health. Finally, we have seen that the Uranist is frequently inflicted with a congenital nervous affection to which most of the discomfort from which he suffers must be attributed.

When one meets a Uranist who exhibits signs of a serious nervous affection or of psychic disorders it would be wrong to attribute them to the satisfaction of his homosexual urge: these are only the special symptoms of a nervous disease from which he suffers. Krafft-Ebing believes that there are certain Uranists who can repress their urge through a refinement of feelings and will-power. But he likewise points out the danger incurred by these individuals as a result of their enforced abstinence of falling into neurasthenia and cerebral disorders. Since it is proven that abstinence aggravates the

Uranists' morbid conditions we need to encourage them in their homosexual acts. We have already shown why it would be wrong to believe that in abstaining from the homosexual act the Uranist is brought to practice coition with women. Tarnowsky is even of the opinion that Uranists who fail in their attempts at normal coition frequently become hysterical.

Sexual excess is just as harmful to the Uranist's health as to that of the normal man. It is quite evident that the pederast of whom Hammond speaks, and who performed the unnatural act eleven times during the same night must have been exhausted. On the other hand, the fact is not surprising that immediately after the homosexual act, the Uranist feels a state of well-being similar to that resulting from coition performed under normal physiological conditions.

Since the reasons which are generally given to justify the penalties against Uranists are not of the nature to establish such justification, we may ask whether there do not exist other motives for repressing unnatural acts. We have seen that some Uranists can have intercourse only with those men who do not belong to their social order. One could say then that the punishment enacted by the law prevents the lowering of the morals of normal men whose temperaments through intercourse with Uranists would in the long run become Uranistic. This point ought to be carefully explained. It seems according to the data which we have now at hand concerning the problem that the normal male adult who gives himself to Uranistic practices never acquires a homosexual urge in this way. It would be wrong to take for sexual inversion the state in which a normal man finds himself after having given himself to a Uranist for the first time from avarice and finally surmounts all his disgust for homosexual practices. There is no fear of such a danger for the relations between a normal man and a Uranist generally consists of the latter's satisfaction through masturbation, and the accomplishment of that act rarely causes the normal individual to feel any sexual excitement. Men who give themselves to Uranists for money clearly merit our contempt as much as prostitutes whose profession hardly contributes to the elevation of character. But since we tolerate prostitution in women there is no reason why we should not tolerate it in man. It is not the modern legislators' business to suppress masculine prostitution. The present laws can only favor its expansion for whose effective control the police unfortunately have no means whatever. Besides, even admitting that the normal man's danger of becoming a Uranist himself through giving himself to Uranists really exists, an hypothesis which no fact can confirm, the objection can no longer hold when we consider the intercourse between Uranists themselves. It is therefore our right to ask whether legal provisions based on this hypothesis would not assure the freedom from punishment of the Uranist who satisfies his urge with other Uranists, while striking those who satisfy it with normal men, either alone or together with their accomplices. Lisst approaches the problem from another direction; he asks that the law strike only those who make a profession of pederasty hoping in this way to check masculine prostitution.

We are told that in placing no obstacle whatever in the path of homosexual relations we would favor the development of a sort of psychic epidemic of sexual inversion. I believe this belief to be ill-founded; indeed, it is hardly probable that a man enjoying a normal sexual urge would to perform homosexual acts for the sole reason that they are not legally prohibited. If that were so we would today undoubtedly see many normal men practicing mutual onanism which is not prosecuted by the law. It is an act which is not generally practiced when persons are not pushed to it by a predisposition to sexual inversion. Sexual inversion has never become epidemic in countries in which it does not fall under the application of the law.

It could also be said that the law takes sufficient account of the urge of Uranists in tolerating certain homosexuals practices, as mutual masturbation for example. But this objection is valueless: we have indeed seen that the desire of Uranists manifests itself in very different forms; there are, for example, those who find satisfaction only in the application of the member on some part of the body while mutual masturbation attracts them no more than does solitary onanism.

Present legislation is illogical on several points. All the reasons raised against unnatural matings could be likewise applied to mutual masturbation which is tolerated by the law. Objections raised on the grounds of morals, health, and other similar considerations may be applied with equal value to all unnatural acts, no matter what they may be. It is my opinion that from the legislator's standpoint no valuable objection can be raised whatsoever against unnatural matings any more than against mutual onanism. Legislation also presents another contradiction: in Germany sexual intercourse between women is not punished at all; they are allowed to practice any sexual acts they desire. It may be that the entire absence of penalties in regard to women is due to the fact that when the legislation concerning unnatural practices was put into effect there was no data on the nature of their sexual relations. It is none the less true that at present women may perform with impunity those acts for which men would be prosecuted, such as licking each other's genitals.

When a law is discussed we must of necessity determine whether its practical application produces good or bad results. Since we are discovering that the law which punishes unnatural matings has produced rather bad effects in protecting the band of exploiters we should naturally ask whether its abrogation would not be more profitable to the morale, to the maintenance of morals, and to the people's respect of the law.

The Uranist ought to be prosecuted when he violently forces an other to commit the sexual act. In many cases the Uranist is led on by the irresistible force of his urge so that under certain circumstances his act should be regarded as a pathological phenomenon and not as a crime. However a violent act evidently causes damage to the victim and to society to the same extent as does the rape of a girl, and it is the duty of the State to prevent it. If an individual is forced to commit a violation through a pathological cause and by a power which he is incapable of mastering, society ought to place him in an insane asylum instead of a prison. Any man who causes damage to society ought to be isolated: the criminal is put into prison; the madman is shut up in an asylum. Society should have the right to deal severely with the Uranist who provokes a public scandal. It is forbidden to perform an obscene act in public, just as it is forbidden to all men to behave publicly towards a woman in a manner which is perfectly allowable in the absence of witnesses.

When a male adult freely gives himself to Uranistic practices it appears to me that the law ought not to be in a position to oppose him therein. However, I believe that this man to do so should pass a certain age and that the law should prevent Uranists from satisfying themselves with young boys. Children under a certain age, sixteen or eighteen, for example, ought to be carefully protected by the law because they have not yet the necessary judgment for conducting themselves properly, and because boys before the age of puberty, being able to acquire sexual inversion through relations with Uranists, also run the risk of being perverted and of losing all moral sense. The law ought therefore to protect them by enacting penalties always in their favor against Uranists. As to the age at which the young man should escape this guardianship I would place it at sixteen or eighteen. Another may be chosen; I do not choose to commit myself on this point.

It is impossible to deny the fact that Uranists may be counted by the thousands and that consequently the State should act justly towards them. The satisfaction of one of the most imperious urges can not be placed by the law on the same footing with a common crime. In studying the judicial statutes I discovered that for some time the judgments therein have become less severe and that the penalties for unnatural matings are relatively lenient. I believe that in all cases the courts treated leniently individuals really inflicted with a morbid sexual urge. But any penalty no matter how light has the bad effect of banning from society

most of those it strikes; it is often sufficient merely to make
a legal inquiry to render social relations entirely impossible
for those persons implicated in it.

Since the State, in prosecuting Uranists, has the safeguard
of morals in view; since, on the other hand, it is an established
fact that such individuals are not guilty—that their incriminating acts are necessary for the satisfaction of a morbid
urge, inherent in their nature—only one means of suppression
remains to the State: that of the interment of Uranists in
insane asylums. Prisons are made for criminals; we can no
longer at the present time consider as criminals those inflicted
tainted with sexual inversion.

"Any woman, practicing prostitution under police supervision shall be punished with imprisonment if she violates
the rules established for the safeguard of the public health,
of public order, and of decency, or if she practices prostitution
without being under said police supervision." This paragraph gives the police a sufficiently effective means of controlling feminine prostitution: they can prevent prostitutes
from operating in certain streets. It is to be regretted that
a similar provision has not been enacted for dealing with
masculine prostitution. Male prostitutes are entirely at liberty
to follow their calling without being molested by the investigation of the police or of the courts. They escape all government inspection. The government is not armed against the
masculine underworld because the laws aim at only certain
forms of intercourse between men. This state of things
would not exist if the above law applied to men as well as
women; it could, for example, be modified to read as follows:
"Any person, practicing prostitution shall be,——etc." There
is no justice in giving male prostitutes liberty which is refused their female prototypes; nor is there any more justice
in leaving to the mercy of a narrow and harsh provision of
legislation the Uranist who seeks to satisfy his sexual urge
in a manner comformable to his Uranistic nature.

Chapter XIII

SEXUAL INVERSION IN WOMEN

Sex Acts Between Women; Historic Lesbians; General Characteristics; Manners, Walk, etc.; Sexual Urge in Women; Types of Sex Acts; Fetichism, Sadism, etc.; Theory of Lesbianism; The Doctor and Lesbians.

I shall devote this chapter to sexual inversion in women without however going deep into the subject. If I give it a restricted place in comparison with what I have given the study of sexual inversion in man it is not because I consider the subject less important from a practical point of view. I have determined to follow this procedure for several reasons, first of all, we have much less data on the phenomenon of inversion between women, and we know very little about the homosexuality of women in history. However, I am quite sure that a great many of them present the urge. In the second place, there are many points in the study of inversion in women which become easy to treat after a study of inversion in man: for example, the treatment of that disease, its diagnosis, etc. A third reason is due to our customs and usages which permit women to entertain relations between themselves with greater facility than men. Finally, there is no need to talk of legislation since in Germany the Penal Code in no way suppresses homosexual acts between women.

220

In Germany, homosexual intercourse between women is legally permissible. It is otherwise in Austria by virtue of Article 129 of the Penal Code. Naturally, if the act is accompanied by aggravating circumstances, as violence or public scandal, it is prosecuted by German law. The following is Hofmann's opinion on this point: "In no case are the sexual acts performed only by women of the same importance as pederasty from the standpoints of morality, and especially of penal law." My opinion is different for I do not make any distinction between intercourse among men and intercourse among women; why should the former be more immoral than the latter? I find, for example, that the cunnilingus of women ought not be considered other than the pressing of the member against the other's body. When we are dealing with a morbid desire immunity from legal punishment seems to me to be desired in both cases. These reasons sufficiently explain the relative briefness with which I shall treat of sexual inversion in women.

Sexual perversion in women is similar in all points to that in men. The rather strange practices employed by women should not in many cases be connected with a morbid urge. Mantegazza mentions the fact that certain ladies employ their little pet dogs for a sexual purpose. I know a married woman who had trained her dog to lick the genitals until complete satisfaction ensued. She confessed this habit to me herself, fearing that she had contracted a disease therefrom. I know another woman whose tendencies are quite sadistic. Ordinary coition gives her no enjoyment. "I wish," she says, "that the sexual act did not exist and was replaced by the bites which I would give my husband and which he would give me."

There are all sorts of sexual perversions in women; but that which appears most often is the inversion in which women feel themselves attracted not by men as they should normally but towards other women. This urge is similar to that of the Uranist which we have already studied in detail. Women with a homosexual urge have received different appelations and I shall later return to some of these. Ulrichs calls them Uranists and says that their number is about the same as that of male Uranists.

In antiquity love among women is said to have been very widespread in the island of Lesbos. Sappho, the poetess, is said to have indulged in it. Virey and some other authors hold this to be true; others, Monecaut, for example, claims that Sappho has been wrongly reproached with it, and that she simply employed with some exaggeration the word love for friendship. I should say that Monceaut despite all the care he took in writing his book on love cannot be considered from the standpoint of sexual inversion as an infallible critic for he appears to be hardly acquainted with that subject. It seems to me that Sappho's poems indeed treat of love among women but that is not why she did not also sing of the legitimate love between men and women, and even if it were otherwise, it should not be concluded that Sappho herself practiced love among women; she probably wished simply to depict in her poems the tendencies of the women of her time.

According to Ploss tribadism was likewise quite widspread in ancient Rome and it was practiced with women provided with an abnormally large clitoris. These women were called *frictices* or *subigatrices*.

Ploss relates that mutual masturbation in women is quite frequent in the Orient. According to him women who give themselves to it may succeed by means of constant masturbation of the clitoris in artificially giving that organ such dimensions as to permit them to practice tribadism. Tribadism has always been quite widespread in the Orient above all among the Arabs. Mantagazza observes that women confined in harems frequently practice this particular form of love.

Zyro quotes Pouqueville who stated that the languid women in the harem of the Sultan, who always preferred love in the manner of the Greeks to natural love, served as lovers to their female companions. Virey tells us of deeds of the Orient of the same type which are confirmed by numerous passages from Oriental poetry.

There is a popular Arabian song in which a husband la-

ments about his wife. The following is a passage, according
to the translation by Buckert:

"God gave me a wife, who is as slim as a bean
  Thieving and bold as the crow and the magpie;
  In love with the women, she despises the men
  And delights herself only with riff-raff and rabble."

Ploss relates that a King of Siam having learned that his
concubines practiced tribadism among themselves punished
them severely. He also says that German women of the
Middle Ages made an open display of this custom. He cites
as proof of his assertion the list of punishments inflicted by
the Church which were drawn up at Worms in the eleventh
century by the Bishop Burchard and in which he spoke of
sexual relations among women.

A series of cases, which have been collected in a work of
Tegg's has been pointed out as having formerly taken place
in England. They deal with women who were taken for
men and several of whom even married other women. These
events happened for the most part in the eighteenth century.
We likewise have in our possession the observations of Parent
Duchatelet on the passionate love among women.

Ulrichs reports quite a series of historic anecdotes on
women who practiced tribadism but their authenticity is not
sufficiently proved. This proof, moreover, would be difficult
to obtain. For example, he names Catherine Howard, wife
of Henry VIII of England, as being a Uranist, to use his own
expression, and he believes she was condemned to death because of her homosexual habits. History gives reason for
the execution of Queen Catherine her relations with her
grandfather's servants.

Literature has furnished us with numerous documents.
Chevalier believes that novelists generally make a study of
homosexual love in women more willingly than its counterpart in men because it appears less repulsive. We find numer-
out novels of the French naturalist school treating of this
subject. Diderot had already developed the theme in his

"Religieuse." During our own time Zola in his novel called "Nana" very explicitly describes the liaison between the heroine and her friend Satin. Chevalier also names in the novelists who have utilized this theme Balzac who delighted in depicting certain sexual inversions. In one of his novels, he recounts the love of a woman for a eunuch.

It has been asked in what social plane tribadism is the most popular. This problem is very difficult to solve for women can keep their desires a secret even better than men. It was my intention to give an account of it as detailed as possible for the City of Berlin, and I owe a great part of the results that I have been able to obtain the confidences that women inflicted with sexual perversion have been willing to make to me. I have been fortunate enough also to meet several habitues of feminine Uranist circles who furnished me with certain documents. I have received some valuable detailed information from a woman who after several years of married life was separated from her husband to give herself up freely to her homosexual urge and who now lives maritally with another woman. Most of my researches in the field of homosexuality in women have been made in collaboration with my friend Dr. Dessoir.

Sexual intercourse among female Uranists may be discovered in all circles: for example, among actresses as well as among barmaids. I can testify that there are married women who are inflicted with sexual inversion and who do not hesitate to satisfy their desire. But it is especially among prostitutes that one finds tribades in great numbers. I know from an authoritative source that 25 per cent of the prostitutes of Berlin have sexual intercourse among themselves.

When two of these women live together in the same apartment only one of them is a prostitute: the other lives with her friend as a lady's maid or as a tenant. We shall later see that in the relations between women the active and passive roles are often very distinct; the women who fill them call themselves "father" and "mother," respectively. In legitimate marriage it is agreed that the man may permit himself several marital degressions but the woman must observe absolute fidelity to him; likewise in the liaison between two women, only the "father," the woman who plays the active role, has the right to have intercourse with men. I have been told that there are numerous exceptions to this rule, and that the one, for example, who has the physical advantage whether she plays the active or the passive role, is often a prostitute.

The persons who gave me this information could not tell me whether among "virgins" there are a large proportion of tribades. I believe that among virgins as well as worldly women one could find cases of sexual perversion. Coffignon says that the aristocracy furnishes the greatest number of women practicing tribadism.

The women who surrender themselves to their homosexual urge generally receive the surname of "Bloated." When two women keep house together they are said to have contracted a bloated marriage of a bloated liaison. In certain cases the name of "Platonic friendship" is preferred. In Vienna, if we are to believe a patient of Krafft-Ebing's, they give themselves the surname of "Uncle."

These women are also called tribades; however, several authors reserve the name of tribadism for a special designation, *clitoris in vaginam alterius,* and call those women who indulge in this practice tribades. The expression Lesbian love is also used, in memory of the Isle of Lesbos; but this term is applied more particularly to the act which brings on the orgasm by the licking of the genitals. The "woman-licker" is called cunnilingua, and the entire act cunnilingus; this word is also applied to the same act as practiced by a man on a woman.

The physiognomy and the external manners of tribades are generally not peculiar. I conclude from the observations that I have been able to make that the women whose faces are covered with hair like those of men are not for that reason particularly predisposed to sexual inversion. The genitals of tribades are not abnormal. Sometimes these women are masculine in their manners above all and in their facial traits.

The evolution of the homosexual urge varies according to the individual. A great many tribades remain a very long time unconscious of their condition. One of them told me that she came to understand years later many episodes of her youth which were for her a closed book. She was a governess for a long time and she recalled that at the age of sixteen she loved to put on boys' clothes during the absence of the master. She experienced therein a feeling of well-being. She now wears men's apparel whenever she can. Her "mother," that is to say, the friend who plays the passive role with her has forbidden her to do so. In every other respect she carefully avoids anything that could lead to a scandal in the house due to the relations she has with her friend.

I know another young woman inflicted with sexual inversion who did not recognize the fact for years. At the age of eighteen she listened with astonishment to her companions who went into ecstasy about having the good fortune of knowing a young man and being embraced by him. She could not imagine what pleasure women could feel therein and found the company of pretty women much preferable to that of good-looking young men. Thus she went through life naive and unconscious of her condition until the age of twenty. It was a friend of hers who initiated her.

It would be wrong to believe that homosexual women are distinguished by certain faults in their character: on the contrary, there are many of them who detest lies and all vices in general. In childhood they willingly play the games of little boys and abandon dolls. Those who play the role of "father" love to clothe themselves as men; however, there is no absolute rule for this. I have seen some tribades who dressed as men but who played the passive roles with their friends.

They have many masculine habits; some smoke cigars. A tribade has told me that she began at the age of five to smoke strong cigars, which she has always preferred to cigarettes; they have never caused her any discomfort.

Their occupations are often quite masculine. When the

woman whose urge is homosexual also possesses the character of a man, she is known as a "virago."   The following is
Krafft-Ebing's description of the virago: "She is quite young
when the homosexual urge appears in her: as a little girl, her
favorite games are those of boys; she holds dolls in contempt
and has a passion for the rocking-horse; she plays at soldiers
and brigand. She does not like needle-work, and is awkward
at it. Her untidy manner of dressing gives her the appearance of a street urchin. She tends more towards the sciences
than towards artistic accomplishments. She smokes and
drinks and she detests perfumes and frills. She bitterly reflects on her being born a woman and on her not being able
to lead the free existence of a student or of a soldier. She will
go in with Amazonian ardor for young men's sports. This
masculine soul enclosed in a feminine body gives her courage
and virile sentiments. Her hair is cut short; the cut of her
dress is like that of men's clothing; her greatest desire is to
wear the latter in their entirety. She takes as her ideal those
women of history or of her own time who were distinguished
for their intelligence and their activity."

One of Westphal's patients had a talent for mechanical
construction. Female occupations in which male Uranists
attain great facility have for tribades no attraction. One of
them told me that she could not tolerate needle-work and
that she did the house-work not because she found pleasure
in it but because of her role of mother in her relations with
her friend.

The tribades' bearing is masculine only when they are not
being watched. When they realize they are being observed
or when they are not among their own kind they assume feminine mannerisms, under which they hide their real nature. I
know some in whom it would have been impossible for me to
detect the slightest external sign of their sexual urge.

But it is quite different when the tribade abandons herself
to her real nature. I recall having one day seen a tribade in
masculine attire; an artificial moustache covered her upper
lip. By her walk, by her manner of handling cigars, and by

her manner of greeting, I mistook her for a man. She was a very well-known tribade in Berlin and no one would have suspected her real sex unless he already knew it. My surprise was great when I was told that the individual in question was a woman.

Tribades find great pleasure in dancing, provided it is with another woman: they do not dance willingly with men. Their life is passionate like that of Uranists. When it is shared they are completely happy. But the thought that they cannot have a family because of the antipathy they have for sexual intercourse with men is sometimes painful to them. According to confidences made to me the dread of masculine contact is much less violent in tribades than in Uranists who attempt normal coition. It is clear that the antipathy of the woman for the man cannot have from the standpoint of coition the same importance as that of the Uranist for the woman: for in the latter case the erection is a prerequisite. We have seen that the same thought also troubles Uranists. When the tribade's love is thwarted she may become the victim of serious disorders of the nervous system and even of a fierce frenzy. Virey tells us that Soranus was acquainted with this fact: tribades, he says, chase young girls with a fury of which men would hardly be capable.

Tribades, unlike Uranists, do not give themselves masculine Christian names. A well-known tribade whose name I keep secret and whose first name I even change is called "Fritz o' the cuffs" because she always wears large cuffs. Like Uranists tribades claim to be able to recognize each other merely by looking at each other, by the manner of meeting, greeting, etc. A great many of them have affirmed this to me. As to what there may be in their glances which permit them to distinguish those who belong to their world, I could not say. According to conversations I have had with other tribades a phenomenon is involved which we have already discovered in Uranists: they look at other women in the same way that men look at pretty women in the street. If the persons they thus look at exchange their glances, in order to convey the

idea that their interest is reciprocated, the desired result is
obtained. Very often it is not only the glance but also the
walk and the manners which contribute to the recognition of
a tribade. The glances they exchange are charged with desires as are those exchanged by Uranists; but one should not
believe that they possess any special significance. Certain
movements of the lips likewise allow them to disclose without pronouncing a word the exact nature of the act which
they propose and to make known by varying this movement
whether they will play the active or the passive role. Tribades make use of different ways of becoming acquainted.
One of these is advertising; when a woman advertises for a
friend there can be no doubt as to her intentions. Sometimes
they become acquainted on the street.

The homosexual urge in women has the same peculiarities
as its parallel in men. A tribade feels herself attracted to a
very definite type of woman. One of them has told me that
her desires could be satisfied only with tall blondes; contact
with little brunettes was for her intolerable. There are some
who are constant in their attachments; others, on the contrary, love changes and seek a new friend every day. The
persons from whom I have this information claim that some
of these attachments may last a very long time. I have been
told of one that has continued thus for seventeen years. I
know of another in its seventh year. In the latter case the
liaison is regarded by the tribades involved as a veritable
marriage.

The tribade households are frequently troubled by scenes
of jealousy and by fights which generally end in reconcilia-
tion. Zola gives us a very fine description of the jealousy
evinced by Nana who threatens to slap Madame Robert because of Satin. He likewise depicts the jealousy of a lover
of Nana's, who wants to provoke Satin to a duel. Any
thwarting of their love is felt deeply by these women, morally
as well as physically. Westphal cites the case of one of them
who because of it completely lost her sleep and her appetite.

When their liaison is broken they often become the victims of the greatest despair.

In what way do tribades succeed in completely satisfying their genital senses? There is one way, which consists of introducing the clitoris in the other's vagina, thus procuring enjoyment for both. Aristophanes rails against a Milesian custom, which employed an artificial penis during the sexual act. I do not know whether this mode is often practiced. It is not a rule in all cases if I am to rely on what has been told me. There is no clitoris no matter how big which would permit a woman to accomplish this act. The juxtaposition and the rubbing of the genital organs ought to be sufficient in causing enjoyment in both women at the same time. Mantegazza believes the habitual intercourse among women results in increasing the size of the clitoris; but he does not give any proof and his assertion may be doubted. Forberg believes that the clitoris may attain a length sufficient to perform the complete sexual act; but, according to Casper Liman, the fact has never been observed.

If I am to believe the information I have received, it is above all by licking the genitals that tribades accomplish the sexual act. In this case, the "woman-licker" plays the active role, the other, the passive. Coffignon believes that tribades can exchange roles but much rarer than pederasts. I do not know what takes place in Paris but in Berlin these roles remain strictly separate. A tribade named X declared to me that she had never enjoyed the act herself unless she herself licked the other's genitals and when I asked her whether she could take the passive role she replied that she would not be at all excited by it. I also recall that she became indignant, just as a normal man would be, when I asked her whether she would not like to practice coition with a man.

On the other hand, I know one of these "mothers" who has never succeeded in playing the active role: that is to lick the other's genitals. Inversion of the roles seems to both parties concerned disagreeable and repulsive. I believe that in all liaisons of this type one would discover this marked distinction between the "father" and the "mother." This same X, of whom I have just spoken had already had a previous liaison which she had broken because her friend wanted her to play the passive role to which she would never consent. In other cases the parts are not separated so clearly. Each of the women takes the passive part in turn, for example, when neither finds pleasure in the active part.

There still remain many obscure phases of the problem, and the data which we posses is often contradictory. A tribade told me, in opposition to the information I received from others—and she seemed trustworthy—that in her opinion, the active role could never give pleasure to the one who filled it. If we wish to pass our opinion in the matter we must approach it from different angles for the facts disclosed evidently present numerous variations. The example of the two tribades filling each role in turn ought not lead us to the false generalization that the active and passive roles are not clearly differentiated. I believe that one could find examples corroborating either one of the two opinions.

The act accomplished by licking the woman's genitals is also called Sapphism, from the name of Sappho, the poetess. Martineau, in his "Lectures on Vulvular and Anal Malformations," describes under the name of Sapphism that form of sexual inversion in which the clitoris is excited by the tongue: but that requires the cooperation of two women, the one active, the other passive. This act is very popular among tribades; I know of only one household of women in which it does not take place often; the one who ordinarily plays the active role and whose genital excitability is very great, would ask nothing better than to practice it, but the "mother" who is of a calmer temperament, refused to give herself to it.

It is a certainty that many women inflicted with sexual inversion practice masturbation. Sometimes one of them also masturbates a friend and caresses her genitals and legs: Krafft-Ebing and Westphal have seen examples of it. Those who masturbate themselves think of young girls during the act.

To conclude there are a great many who have no sexual relations of any sort. Some are prevented by their social position; others content themselves with platonic liaisons like those we have already cited apropos of Uranists. Their voluptuous dreams always relate to the perversions of love.

There are among women affected with sexual inversion, a great many who are married. It seems however that most of them evince only a lukewarm desire for marriage. A lady whom I know of homosexual tendencies married only to pose as a married woman to travel with her husband and for other similar reasons; but she was separated from her husband after six years of married life. Marriage could not agree with her. She was obliged to satisfy her homosexual desires, to have unknown to her husband relations with a tribade. Tribades consider marriage only as an accessory.

Some of them are psychic hermaphrodites—in this presenting an analogy with certain Uranists: their desires are directed alternatively to men and to women. It may happen that a woman who up to a certain time has been in love with other women may then meet a man to whom she feels attracted. She may love and marry him. However, love for men in women who clearly manifest a homosexual urge is never anything but a fleeting episode in their lives. They are seized after a length of time, and with the same violence, by their desire for women.

Normal coition does not suffice to satisfy the tribade's sexual needs. I know one who makes her husband lick her genitals in order to experience enjoyment; ordinary coition leaves her entirely indifferent. The cunnilingus practiced by her husband is for her less disagreeable; sometimes she even experiences voluptuous sensations therein without having to think of a woman. I know of other cases in which the cunnilingus of the husband cannot cause the same voluptuous feelings in the tribade that are felt by her while practicing the same act with a woman. A woman of my acquaintance was separated from her husband when she discovered that conjugal relations could not no matter what means was employed give her the satisfaction of her genital needs.

Mantegazza believes that many unhappy families which are broken up for no apparent reason are due to the homosexual tendencies of the wives. This appears to me rather questionable, the more so since in this regard I know married women who often entertain relations with tribades unknown to their husbands. Martineau likewise knows examples of it. Duhousset published a case of sexual inversion which is so strange that it is hardly believable. It involves two women who had had sexual relations. After marrying, one of them renewed her liaison with her old girl friend who became pregnant. It must therefore be supposed, unless the whole story is a hoax, that the married woman had in passing from the arms of her husband to those of her friend transferred to the latter a small quantity of sperm.

I can give no precise information on the tendencies of fetichism, masochism and sadism in women tained with sexual inversion. There seem to be women of homosexual tendencies who desire young immature girls. Tardieu tells of a woman who had sexual relations with little girls of six to eleven. There is also the case of a mother who with her hands deflowered her daughter aged ten and who for many years continued daily to introduce her fingers into the young girl's vagina and anus. Certain women whose experience in the matter is not to be doubted have told me that they have heard about such phenomena in connection with sexual intercourse between men and women, but that they had never heard of anything of such nature in the relations among tribades. All I know of the matter is that the active partner in a liaison between women required the other to wear men's shirts and short trousers.

We know of other cases in which the tendency to sexual inversion appeared periodically and other psychic anomalies. It is known for example that in some women this desire appears during the menstrual periods; between the menses although the sexual tendencies are never absolutely normal the perversion is very slight.

As to the etiology of sexual perversion in women we must take for granted the existence of a natural predisposition just as we did in the case of man. Krafft-Ebing here also differentiates between congenital and acquired inversion as an example of acquired inversion, he gives the case of the celebrated Ilma S. through whom he made his remarkable researches in hypnotism. This person at first had intercourse with a man she loved; her desire for women appeared later. She claimed that she had lost the power of loving men because she had abandoned herself, body and soul, to the love she had for her cousin. She believed that after this great love she would be incapable of loving another man being as she said one of those who loved only once in their lives. Without stopping to determine whether women are indeed not inclined to love more than once which is quite probable Krafft-Ebing places this case in the group involving acquired inversion. On the other hand he cites very many examples of congenital inversion. Westphal is of the opinion that sexual inversion in women is entirely congenital. Very often it appears quite early in life. One of Westphal's patients presented the phenomenon of inversion at the age of seven when she already had a passion for women and tried by caresses and playfulness to force them to masturbate her.

In many cases sexual inversion in women is found to be caused by accidental causes. Habitial homosexual relations are given as causes of sexual inversion. We have seen that the same etiological cause is given to Uranism. Hofmann gives a few points in his "Legal Doctor's Manual" throwing some light on this point: He claims that tribadism must be very widespread in prisons and in houses of detention where prostitutes are sent. The following is the dictum of Dr. Fischer, a prison doctor of large experience: "As Mayer says it often happens that young girls used to sexual pleasures form liaisons among themselves even in the jails. Their passions become very keen, they quarrel through love and jealously just as lovers do." I believe that most authors here confuse the cause with the effect. The truth of the matter is that among prostitutes there are a great many women inflicted with sexual inversion, and when they are in prison their inclination is disclosed to the eyes of the observer but the latter would be wrong in attributing their inversion to their stay in prison. But I believe that what are often taken for real causes are only those circumstances which occasion the patient's giving free rein to her inclination for the first time, or which make her realize the true nature of her desires until then latent. In other words they are external conditions which awake from unconsciousness the urge in question. We have seen that the same is true of Uranists.

Sexual inversion in women is also attributed to an hereditary neuropathic condition. However, if I am to rely on the results of my inquiries the facts do not always confirm this opinion. Moreover, it is often discovered that besides sexual inversion there are other disorders such as periodic insanity and hysterical epilepsy.

The following is a case which shows how a very secondary external condition may lead a woman to realize her abnormal state. It deals with a person named X, today thirty years of age; she lost her virginity at the age of fifteen at the hands of a young man whom she never saw again and who produced a disagreeable impression on her. The recollection of the sexual act was likewise painful to her. Later she made the acquaintance of another young man whose looks pleased her, and with whom she had intercourse a number of times finding in the sexual act complete voluptuous satisfaction. Towards the age of eighteen after having had intercourse with several men she met a young girl who approached and embraced her and placed her hands on her breasts. The latter contact immediately caused her very keen enjoyment in which she exults even today. Besides, she greatly likes the caresses which women are in the habit of giving each other. A short while after her new friend invited her to go to bed with her and there Y practiced cunnilingus on her. The roles were then reversed and they continued to live together taking the active and passive roles in turn. From that time on X no longer found pleasure in intercourse with men. She could satisfy her sexual urge only by a homosexual act. She had men practice cunnilingus on her without feeling any voluptuous sensation at all. She has been living with a girl friend for eight years with whom she experiences and to whom she gives complete satisfaction of the genital instinct.

One will agree with me when I say that the casual contact with a woman such as the embracing of X and the young girl she found sympathetic cannot be considered as the determining cause of sexual inversion. The ground was prepared and the foregoing circumstance only awakened an abnormal predisposition which if it did not manifest itself then would surely have appeared sooner or later on the occasion of a similar incident. We have seen in speaking of Uranists that there are some in whom the homosexual state remains latent for quite a while, until some accidental event forces the patient to be convinced of the reality of his abnormal desire.

Sometimes, as an explanation of homosexual tendencies in men or women, we hear people make the most inaccurate statements. Thus, a tribade attributed the cause of her sexual state to the sensations she experienced in cunnilingus whose intensity surpass anything to be felt in normal coition. There is nothing astonishing in the fact that a tribade loses her desire for normal coition; we likewise see the habit of masturbation destroy, in man, the desire for coition and even the possibility of practicing it. The explanation given me by this woman recalls that of Stark and Mantegazza apropos of sexual inversion in man. Both seem to forget that the essential fact is the desire which urges the tribade towards the woman, instead of forcing her to seek relations with man: cunnilingus practiced on her by a man gives her only moderate pleasure and even none; performed by a woman, the same act gives her the most intense voluptuous feelings.

From a medical standpoint what we have said of Uranism applies just as well to tribadism. The diagnosis naturally presents still greater difficulties when it deals with the feminine sex for the women are still more hesitant about confessing than men and they decide more rarely than men to consult a physician on the subject of a sexual perversion. But since this perversion really exists the physician ought to be in a position to treat it in women as well as in men.

The subject is always very delicate to broach in the presence of a woman. However, the physician may obtain a response from his patient by talking to her in private as he does in the case of a Uranist. One would do well in dealing with a married woman to keep the husband away for she naturally wishes to confide only in the doctor and not in her husband who may be but a poor judge in the matter. The physician shall have first to caution the woman that the only treatment possible is a psychic one. Mantegazza believes that a cure may easily be effected provided it is attempted soon after marriage but that later it would become impossible. This opinion seems to me ill-grounded. Theoretically, I maintain that sexual inversion is curable, but I strongly doubt whether its cure would be very easy and lasting.

FINIS